Contents

Acknowledgements

The authors and publishers are grateful to the following examination boards for permission to reproduce their questions:

- The Associated Examining Board (AEB)
- The Northern Examinations and Assessment Board (NEAB)
- The Northern Ireland Council for Curriculum Examinations and Assessment (NICCEA)
- Oxford and Cambridge Schools Examination Board (Oxford and Cambridge)
- Oxford Delegacy of Local Examinations (Oxford)
- University of Cambridge Local Examinations Syndicate (Cambridge)
- London Examinations, A Division of Edexcel Foundation (London)

The comments, outline answers and tutors' comments are entirely the responsibility of the authors and have neither been provided nor approved by the examining boards. The University of Cambridge Local Examinations Syndicate/Midland Examining Group bears no responsibility for the example answers to questions taken from its past question papers which are contained in this publication. The University of Cambridge Local Examination Syndicate bears no responsibility for the example answers to questions taken from past UODLE question papers which are contained in this publication. UODLE material is reproduced by permission of the University of Cambridge Local Examination Syndicate. Edexcel Foundation, London Examinations accepts no responsibility whatsoever for the accuracy or method of working in the answers given.

part I
Preparing for the examination

Introduction

The aim of this book is to help you to pass Physics with really good grades, and certainly to push up the grade you hope to get. It is intended to help you with the core areas of A- and AS-Level Physics, and in Scotland with Higher Grade Physics. It provides the help that experienced examiners can give and you will learn how

▶ to get the examiners on your side
▶ to answer questions correctly
▶ to avoid easily made slips and omissions which can lose you many marks.

This book is in four parts. Part I helps you to plan your revision and prepare for your exams. Part II covers seven fundamental or core physics topics which all Boards must include in their A-Level syllabuses. Each topic contains

▶ Revision Tips for quick reference
▶ A Topic Outline – essentially some concise revision notes
▶ A Revision Activity to help you think about the topic
▶ Practice questions from a variety of boards

Part III gives you all the answers as well as mark schemes, tips and explanations of answers, and other 'inside information' from the examiners. Part IV contains a mock paper for you to tackle against the clock.

Making the most of this book

We have designed this book for you to *use*. Read it and write in it! Past examination questions have an important part to play in revision, but it is very important to use them only in revision: if you have not first mastered a topic it will be very frustrating to attempt to answer an examination question in full. So begin by looking at the Revision Tips and the Topic Outline *before* you do any writing. If you need to look up more details, consult the *Longman A-Level Study Guide Physics*. This ought to give you enough further detail for your revision. If you need more than this you can try the *Longman A-level Reference Guide Physics* or your textbook.

To help in your revision we have also devised a number of *revision activities* which you can use to vary your approach to revision.

When you have revised the topic and are ready to attempt questions, set an alarm to go off after the same number of minutes as the total number of marks for the question, or for multiple choice questions after two and a half minutes. Where there are spaces provided in the question you can usefully write your answer straight onto the page. The number of lines is a useful guide to the length of your answer, and the number of marks for each part of the question is a rough guide as to how long you should spend on that part.

Answering questions is only the first part of your revision task. The other half of it is checking your answers. Do not be discouraged by wrong answers: remember that you always learn more by your mistakes. The answer section frequently goes into much more detail than you would need to provide in the examination. We have done this in order to help you. We hope that in this way you find the book acts like a kindly teacher or personal tutor.

Lastly, as with the other books in this series, Part IV provides you with an opportunity to try out a whole paper in which you have to practise working against a time constraint. You should use this part, as well as past papers from the board you are taking, to help with your final preparation.

Revising and preparing for the examination

If you have a copy of the *Longman A-Level Study Guide* you will know our story about the snares that can distract the most well-intentioned student from getting down to doing physics homework until a point when it is too late in the evening and the brain is no longer at its most efficient. The same warning applies to revision.

Timing

You need to plan a timetable of work and to keep a record (a diary) of it. You need also to analyse when your best time for working is. Once you know when your best time is, get into a routine of using that time. You must also organise yourself so that you *do* have periodic breaks. After about forty minutes concentration begins to wane. Plan for this kind of break and set yourself a mini-target of revision to be done before it comes up. Ten minutes rest will help you to refresh yourself and enable you to continue your studying more effectively. Stop each study session while you are still making progress and enjoying success. Really good students never leave revision to the last minute. It is best to plan for a large number of short sessions over several weeks than to try to concentrate it all into longer sessions close to the exam.

Location

Where you work is also very important. Try to find somewhere which can be your base, where you can work without being disturbed, and where you can keep your books and papers. Avoid eye strain by making sure that it is a well-lit environment, and make sure that it is comfortable and warm but not overheated. Have everything you need ready at hand: writing paper, pens, a highlighting pencil, calculator, etc.

Engaging in active revision

Once you start work you must work effectively. You will do this if you are interested in what you are doing and if you are well motivated. Above all you need to be *active* in your approach to learning. Just reading a textbook is not enough. That is where this book comes in. Follow our advice on using the topic outline. The text has been written after carefully researching what is in the common syllabuses, and more importantly, what is regularly tested in the core topics of A-Level exams. A temptation to go down interesting side-streets or diversions has been avoided. In your revision you need to have an accurate, organised, and systematic set of notes, expressed in your own words and intelligible to you. But make sure they are *notes*: you already have a textbook and there is no point trying to rewrite it. If you have not already been developing your own notes, then use our topic outlines. The use of a highlighting pencil with your notes or with this book is a good idea.

Start by trying shorter questions or parts of longer questions which have been broken down into structured sub-questions. We also recommend starting on the mathematical parts of a question first, identifying any formulae you will need to use, and sorting out the steps necessary to pursue the calculation to its endpoint. Then move on to the non-mathematical parts of the question. When you get to the end of a topic go back to the text of this book and make sure that there are no parts missing that you should understand.

There is no space in this book to set out questions in the large variety of areas of physics chosen by boards to extend the work of the core, for example in topics such as rigid body mechanics, astrophysics or health physics, to name but a few. But we do hope that the practice of using this book in the core areas will help you establish good working patterns you can use throughout the whole of your particular syllabus.

Examination questions of different types

You need to know which *types* of questions you will encounter in your particular exam. Some boards use comprehension questions, essay or free-response questions and a variety of objective test questions: multiple choice, multiple completion or grid questions. All the examination boards use structured questions and most now offer modular examinations which often consist of several short papers composed of structured questions. Indeed the present trend is for these questions to be the dominant form of questions which is the main reason we have selected so many in this text.

Multiple choice tests

The most common form of multiple choice question is one which consists of a short statement which is to be completed by selecting one of five responses. Only one of the responses is correct and the others are called distractors. These are designed to trap candidates making commonly occurring errors. But there are other types such as the multiple completion type where you have first to decide whether each of, usually, three statements is correct and then choose an answer which corresponds to the correct combination of statements. Normally about forty questions need to be completed in an hour and a half. Multiple choice questions are very good for doing revision even if there will be none in your exam because they can help you find out quickly whether you have understood the topic. Remember you can learn as much from your mistakes as from your correct responses. This book contains a small number of questions of this type. If you find these useful in your revision remember that you can find more in the *Longman A-Level Study Guide*.

Comprehension questions

It is quite common for a comprehension or passage analysis test to be set, the aim being to find out about your communication skills and the way you can apply the concepts you have learned in your course. A passage, sometimes edited from a scientific text, is presented. As well as having to show whether you know enough physics to follow the author's ideas, you may be asked some questions about the consequences of the ideas or you may have to suggest alternative methods or strategies to those in the passage.

If you are to face questions of this type try to get some past examples. Read through the text of one of your examples at a reasonable normal reading speed in order to get an overview of what it is about. Then work through the set questions in order. Where necessary refer back to the passage for greater comprehension and avoid quoting the passage back to the examiners when you are trying to put the answer into your own words. With each question you may find it useful to jot down on rough paper any formulae which may seem applicable. Aim for clear and concise answers which use your knowledge of physics. Don't be tempted to write long rambling sentences. It is common to find that as you get toward the end of the test your understanding increases to a point where you notice mistakes in the answers you had written first. You can then go back and correct these.

Practical tests and data analysis questions

Unless your experimental work is examined by a form of continuous assessment, it is likely that part of your examination will be a practical test. The types of test used by A-Level boards vary considerably. Some boards set a data analysis question where candidates are provided with some data from an experiment already carried out which they must analyse.

Answering a structured question paper
For the reasons already outlined we are concentrating particularly on structured questions. When you actually sit the examination, and particularly if you have to make a choice of questions, you will need to scan the paper quickly and select those which you think you can answer fairly painlessly. These will not necessarily be the questions which are only one or two sentences long. Questions which appear long are sometimes much easier to answer than those which can be read quickly, mainly because the longer questions help you through the exercise and give you more information. Make sure you have read the question fully and understand all the parts of it. Read right through to the end of a question *before* deciding to try it. An easy first part may conceal a sting in the tail which may well carry a high proportion of the marks. Once you are clear about what you are going to do and how you will answer a question, then start work on it. The following list is useful for checking whether you have omitted any important features.

1 If you have drawn a diagram make sure it contains everything that is necessary and relevant. Diagrams should be drawn when specifically asked for, or when you feel that a diagram would be more appropriate and easier for you than a lengthy description. Make sure it is of a reasonable size. Check that the labelling is complete and that key distances are clearly and unambiguously labelled.
2 Definitions should be complete. Do not leave out any constraints or special conditions which should be mentioned.
3 Ensure that any theory is relevant and that conclusions that you draw follow logically from the points you have made. Be concise and try to use each sentence to make a relevant point avoiding both waffle and repetition.
4 In calculations, make sure you include sufficient working to make clear and explain the steps in your answer. If you make a calculator error and there is no evidence as to what you have attempted to do, then the available marks cannot be awarded. When you have reached your final numerical answer check:
    (a) that you have quoted a sensible number of significant figures (2, 3 or 4 at the most would be normal at A-Level)
    (b) that you have included the appropriate units and have used scientific notation with correct powers of ten
    (c) that your answer is sensible and is clearly not absurd.
5 Graphs are used increasingly at A-Level. If you are asked to draw a graph make sure that your axes are clearly labelled and that the units and powers of ten are shown. Choose a convenient scale, plot the points carefully, and draw a best-fit smooth line. Show clearly how any readings, extrapolations, intercepts, or gradients are taken from the graph. When taking readings remember to include units. Remember also that the area under a graph can be significant and that its units are the product of those on the axes.
6 If you are asked (or decide yourself) to include sketch graphs then make sure the axes are clearly labelled.

The most important advice of all is to read a question more than once to make sure you fully understand it. Make sure that you fully understand the command word at the start. These are words like 'describe', 'explain', 'calculate' etc. The following list may help you.

Command words requiring concise answers with the bare minimum of detail
Define A straightforward definition is all that is needed.
State Give a short answer.
Give As 'state'.
Indicate As 'state' but with a little more explanation.

Command words requiring essential but rather more detail

Calculate A numerical answer is required. You should show your working as explained above.

Estimate Like 'calculate', but a precision answer is not expected, and, indeed, may not be possible. Be careful with estimates that you do not quote too many significant figures.

Comment on You should show logically why you are making the statement.

Deduce Similar to 'comment on': you should be logical in your reasoning.

Show or **Show how** Similar to 'deduce'.

Find A rather general term which may mean 'calculate'.

Command words requiring longer reasoned answers supported by relevant facts and principles

Explain, **explain why**, etc. Requires a detailed logical answer.

Describe This is frequently used with reference to a particular experiment. You will need to make sure you have shown all the important steps.

State and explain Rather like 'explain'.

Suggest Frequently used when there is no single correct answer.

How to take examinations

When you set yourself a practice paper, treat it seriously like the real thing. Persuade a relative or friend to start you off, keeping an eye on your time, occasionally letting you know the time elapsed, and telling you when to stop.

Prepare yourself thoroughly for both the practice paper and the real thing. Check the syllabus to see what you will need to take into the examination room and check the regulations to see what you are allowed to take in, especially with regard to calculators. Can you use one in a multiple choice paper and must it be silent, cordless and unable to store and display text and graphics? If the calculator is programmable, you must clear the memory of any programmes – you are not allowed to take the instruction manual into the exam. Make sure you know exactly which formulae and fundamental constants you will be given in the examination. Don't allow yourself any surprises.

Finally, here is advice from the *Longman A-Level Study Guide* which is worth repeating. You will need to employ all the question answering techniques you have been developing. In addition you will need to give close attention to timing. On a multiple choice paper, for example, you should remember that only one mark is allocated to each question. Don't therefore spend too much time on any one question. The questions do not necessarily get more difficult and so do not allow yourself to get stuck on any single question. With the harder questions it is useful to make brief notes on rough paper of your thoughts and decisions. Then when you come to check over your answers at the end you won't have to rethink the question from scratch.

With other kinds of paper you should note the number of questions that you are expected to do and compare this with the total time for the examination. It is very useful to have worked out an approximate time allocation for each question, with some allowance for checking at the end. Remember that you should be scoring marks at a regular rate throughout the examination. The examiner will have a mark scheme that allows the allocation of marks to you for specific points as you make them: remember this and let it caution you against working too slowly on parts of the paper with which you find difficulty.

Lastly remember that examiners are paid-up members of the human race. They do try hard to construct tests which enable you to demonstrate what you know and what you can do, rather than to trap you into showing where you are at your weakest. So think positively and do your best!

Forces in static and dynamic situations

Formulae which you need to be familiar with or to learn. You must be sure which you need to know and which you will be given. Do you know what the symbols represent and can you state the units for each formula?

Pressure = force ÷ area
$$p = \frac{F}{A}$$

Average speed = distance ÷ time taken
$$v = \frac{s}{t}$$

Acceleration = change in velocity ÷ time taken for the change
$$a = \frac{(v - u)}{t}$$

Equations for uniformly accelerated motion
$$v = u + at$$

$$s = \frac{(u + v)}{2} \cdot t$$

$$s = ut + \tfrac{1}{2} at^2$$

$$v^2 = u^2 + 2as$$

Momentum = mass × velocity
$$p = mv$$

Force = rate of change of momentum
$$F = m\frac{(v - u)}{t}$$

$$F = ma$$

Impulse = change in momentum
$$Ft = mv - mu$$

Conservation of momentum formula
$$m_1 u_1 + m_2 u_2 = m_1 v_1 + m_2 v_2$$

Weight = mass × gravitational field strength
$$W = mg$$

Potential energy
$$U = mgh$$

Kinetic energy
$$T = \tfrac{1}{2} mv^2$$

Angular velocity
$$\omega = \frac{2\pi}{T}$$

Centripetal acceleration
$$a = \frac{v^2}{r} = \omega^2 r$$

Tackling problems of static equilbrium

1 Start with a sketch diagram showing all the forces acting on one body.
2 **Resolve** the forces into two components in two mutually perpendicular directions chosen at your convenience (e.g. along a slope and normal to it).

3 Then apply the rule that the **nett** (resultant) force in any particular direction is zero. At this stage if you find an unbalanced force then either you have missed out one or more forces at Step 1 or else you don't have equilibrium.

4 Apply the principle of moments through the most convenient axis.

Tips to remember in dynamics

Newton's first law does not just apply to lone bodies travelling at constant speed in remote regions of space, far away from any forces. Whenever a body travels at constant speed the nett forces acting on it are zero. When a car is travelling at constant speed, all the useful work is being done against resistive forces.

In projectile problems always remember to start by treating the horizontal and vertical motions as independent.

A collision is always inelastic whenever work is done against the internal forces which hold the bodies or structures together, and when there is a consequent, if very small temperature rise.

In circular motion problems the only real force is the centripetal force which causes the inward acceleration towards the centre of the circle. However someone in circular motion *experiences* an apparent outward force which we would call centrifugal force.

TOPIC OUTLINE

Static situations

Physical quantities such as mass, length, time, force and momentum are classed as vectors or scalars. **Scalars** have size only, e.g. $m = 26.0$ kg. **Vectors** have magnitude and direction, e.g. a velocity might be 40 ms^{-1} due north. Scalars are added together by the ordinary rules of arithmetic. Vectors are added by the parallelogram rule which states that if two vectors to be added are represented in magnitude and direction by the sides of a parallelogram, their resultant is represented by the diagonal of the parallelogram.

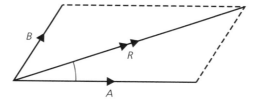

Figure 1.1
Finding the resultant, using the parallelogram rule

Conversely a single vector can be resolved, or broken down into vectors usually perpendicular to each other. The two vectors are called **components**.

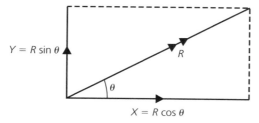

Figure 1.2
Resolving vectors into two components at right angles

$X = R \cos \theta$

$Y = R \sin \theta$

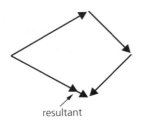

resultant

Figure 1.3

Note that an alternative way of adding two vectors is to draw the vectors as arrows of appropriate length and direction and to place the tail of one arrow on the head of another and then to draw a resultant vector arrow from the tail of the first to the head of the second. With more than two vectors the method is similar.

When a body is at rest, that is in a static situation, it may be in equilibrium under several non-parallel forces acting through a point within it. If so it means that the resultant force is zero and the vector addition method above gives a closed polygon. An example of this occurs in the method of supporting the conducting cable on overhead-wire electrified railways.

Figure 1.4
Three forces in equilibrium

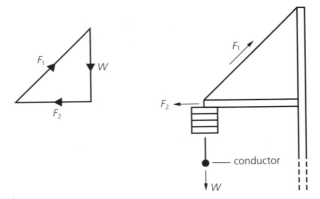

If the resultant force is non-zero of course acceleration results (see below).

A body may also be in equilibrium under several parallel forces acting through different points. A see-saw is the simplest example. Each force on its own produces a **torque** or moment about a fixed axis. The **moment** is defined as the *force × perpendicular distance* from the line of the force to the axis. For equilibrium in this situation the sum of the clockwise moments about *any point* on the body must be equal to the sum of the anticlockwise moments. This statement is known as the **Principle of Moments**.

In static problems a useful concept is that of the Centre of Gravity (Centre of Mass). For an object with a distributed mass the centre of gravity (or centre of mass) is the point at which, for the purpose of calculations, all the mass of the body, and hence all of the weight can be considered to act. This is the point which is used in moment calculations.

If a set of parallel forces do not produce equilibrium then some kind of rotation is produced. It is then useful to introduce the concept of a **couple** which is defined as two equal and opposite parallel forces whose lines of action do not coincide. The moment of a couple is always the same about any fixed point and is always equal to the product of one of the forces and the perpendicular distance between them.

Pressure is defined as the force acting per unit area. In fluids, i.e. liquids and gases, pressure is exerted in all directions. The pressure in a column of liquid is equal to the height × density × gravitational field strength or $h\rho g$.

Dynamic situations

To describe the movement of a body three vector quantities are used: displacement, velocity and acceleration. **Displacement** is the distance 'as the crow flies' from some starting point to the finishing point with the direction also specified. **Velocity** is the rate of change of displacement and **acceleration** the rate of change of velocity. Frequently in A-Level problems the motion is in a straight line, there is no change in direction, and sometimes the scalar term 'distance travelled' is used interchangeably with displacement and the scalar term speed, with velocity.

In A-Level Physics graphs are frequently used. The gradient of a distance-time graph gives the speed of a body, and the gradient of a speed-time graph gives the acceleration. The area under a velocity-time graph is the distance travelled.

In A-Level Physics many examples are confined to the important special case of uniform acceleration in a straight line. If the velocity of a body increases from an initial value u to a final value v, with a constant acceleration a, in a time t, then $a = (v - u)/t$, giving

$$v = u + at$$

and if the displacement is s, then the equations

$$s = \frac{(u + v)}{2} \cdot t$$

$$s = ut + \tfrac{1}{2} at^2$$

and $v^2 = u^2 + 2as$ also hold.

The most common type of acceleration in problems of this kind is where the acceleration a is uniform acceleration under gravity.

A more complicated kind of motion is 'projectile' motion where there are two simultaneous and entirely independent motions. There is accelerated vertical motion described using the equations above, and horizontal motion at a steady speed where the distance travelled s is simply given by $s = vt$. Air resistance and other resistive forces are usually neglected at low speeds, but at high speeds they become dominant until eventually there is no acceleration and a body moves at a constant **terminal** velocity.

Newton's laws of motion use the concept of **momentum**. The vector quantity momentum, p, is defined as mass × velocity i.e. $p = m \times v$.

Newton's laws of motion are:

1 The basic kind of motion is uniform motion in a straight line and a body has this motion unless a resultant force acts on it.
2 If a resultant force acts on a body, the momentum of the body changes and its rate of change of momentum is equal to the resultant force and in the direction of that force. This leads to $F = ma$.
3 Forces between bodies act in pairs, i.e. when one exerts a force (attractive or repulsive) on a second body, the second exerts an equal and opposite force on the first (e.g. the earth attracts me, but I attract the earth with an equal and opposite force).
(See Revision Tips for formulae.)

The **impulse**, I, of a force is defined as the force multiplied by its time of action so when a force acts for a short time dt we get $I = \overline{F}dt = dp$ where $\overline{F}$ is the average force acting over the time interval dt, and dp is the momentum change it produces.

The same change in momentum can either result from a large force acting for a very short time or a much smaller force acting for a much longer time.

Newton's second and third laws combine together to give the principle of the **conservation of linear momentum**. This states that in collisions or interactions between two or more bodies or particles the total momentum remains unchanged, providing of course that no external forces are acting. Collisions where there is also no loss of energy such as those between gas molecules are called **elastic**; in non-microscopic collisions there is usually some loss of energy and the collisions are called **inelastic**.

Energy

Energy is often defined as that which enables a 'job' to be done, a 'job' being the raising of a weight, the acceleration of a mass, etc. In the complete theory of energy and in thermodynamics it is regarded as a *conserved quantity*, changes in energy being merely changes from one form to another. In mechanics, **work** is the amount of energy transferred. If energy is likened to money, then work is like a cheque measuring the money transferred from one account to another.

Work done, W, is defined as the component of the force in the direction of the distance moved multiplied by the distance moved.

$$W = F \times s$$

Energy and work are both measured in joules.

Power is the rate of doing work. Its unit is the watt which is a rate of doing work of $1\,\mathrm{J\,s^{-1}}$. When a body moves forward under a force at a constant velocity v, Power $= F \times v$.

Potential energy is the energy due to the position of a body in a gravitational field, and referred to some level chosen as zero.

Potential energy $= mgh$ where h is the height above the (arbitrary) zero position.

(More generally it also includes other types of stored energy, e.g. energy stored in a spring, in an electric field, or in a magnetic field.)

Kinetic energy is the energy a body has by virtue of its velocity.

Kinetic energy $= \frac{1}{2}\,mv^2$

Uniform circular motion is a kind of motion where the *magnitude* of the velocity vector is constant whilst the direction steadily changes. The velocity is therefore changing and so the particle or body is under acceleration, in this case towards the centre of the circle. By Newton's second law there must be a physical force inwards that is responsible for this acceleration. This force is called a **centripetal** force. It always has a physical cause. In the case of the planets revolving round the sun it is gravitational attraction.

Circular motion

In circular motion it can be more useful to use angular velocity ω measured in radians per second and defined as the angle of a complete revolution in radians, 2π, divided by the time T for a complete revolution in seconds. The relationship between velocity and angular velocity is that $v = \omega r$. Angular acceleration is given by $\omega^2 r$.

Only boards with the rotation of rigid bodies as an option will set more complicated problems.

REVISION ACTIVITIES

Check that you can do the following:

1 Identify which of the following are vectors and which scalars:
force, power, velocity, acceleration, speed, momentum, energy, work done.
2 Write down the units for each of the above.
3 Convert the following so that they are in SI units:
$3300\,\mathrm{mm/s}$; $4.5 \times 10^6\,\mathrm{cm\,s^{-1}}$; $44\,\mathrm{MJ/year}$.

4 Draw velocity-time and acceleration-time graphs for the following types of motion

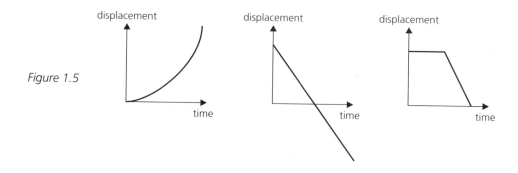

Figure 1.5

5 State Newton's laws of motion in your own words.
6 Distinguish between centrifugal and centripetal force.

(You may also wish to check at this point that you know about the conventions that boards may use for the labelling of graphs. You will not be normally expected to follow these conventions, but should know of them.

PRACTICE QUESTIONS

Question 1
Figure 1.6 shows a wheel, of radius 0.25 m, in contact with a kerb of height 0.10 m. The weight of the wheel, which may be assumed to act at its axle O, is 60 N. A horizontal force F is applied to the axle, so as to roll the wheel over the kerb.

Figure 1.6

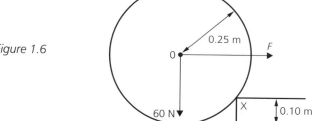

(i) As the wheel just starts to roll over the kerb, a force R on the wheel acts at the corner X of the kerb. On Fig. 1.6 draw the line of action of this force at the instant that the wheel just starts to pivot about X.   *(1 mark)*
(ii) Calculate the moment about X of the weight of the wheel at this instant.

. . . .

. . . .

. . . .

. . . .

. . . .

. . . .

Moment = ...   *(4 marks)*

(iii) Hence calculate the horizontal force F required just to start the wheel to pivot about X.

. . . .

. . . .

. . . .

. . . .

. . . .

$F =$ . . . . *(4 marks)*

(NICCEA)

Question 2

(a) State the conditions for a system of coplanar forces to be in equilibrium.
    (2 marks)

(b) Figure 1.7 shows a crane being used to lift a load of girders, each of which has a mass of 500 kg.

Figure 1.7

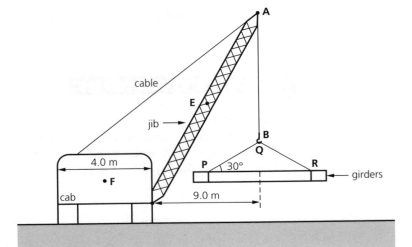

The jib of the crane has a mass of 2500 kg and the cab has a mass of 20 000 kg. The centres of mass (gravity) of the jib and the cab are at their mid-points, **E** and **F** respectively. The hook and cable have negligible mass.

Gravitation field strength, $g = 10 \, \text{N kg}^{-1}$.

 (i) Calculate the tension in the cable **AB** when a single girder is lifted.
      (1 mark)

 (ii) Determine the corresponding tension in the cable **PQR**, when a single girder is lifted. *(2 marks)*

(iii) For the jib in the position shown, determine the tension in **AB** which will just topple the crane. *(2 marks)*

(iv) For the jib in the position shown, determine the maximum number of girders which can be lifted without the crane toppling over.
      (1 mark)

(AEB)

Question 3

(a) Define *acceleration*.

. . . .

. . . . *(1 mark)*

(b) Divers in Acapulco dive from a height of 36 m into the sea. Calculate, ignoring air resistance,
   (i) the time they take to reach the water,

time = ... s

   (ii) their speed of entry into the water.

speed = ... m s^{-1}

(4 marks)

(c) One of the divers referred to in (b) had a mass of 61 kg. In a subsequent free-fall dive from an aircraft, before the parachute was opened, the diver reached a terminal speed of 90 m s^{-1}. Calculate
   (i) the weight of the diver,

weight = ...

   (ii) the force of air resistance on the diver when at the terminal speed,

air resistance = ... N

   (iii) the magnitude and unit of the constant k in the expression

$$\text{air resistance} = kv^2,$$

where v is the speed.

k = ... *(4 marks)*

(d) (i) Use the expression given in (c)(iii) to estimate the air resistance on a diver in (c) moving with a speed of 25 m s^{-1}.

air resistance = ... N

   (ii) Hence comment on whether the instruction in (b) to ignore air resistance is justified.

. . . .

. . . . *(3 marks)*

(Cambridge)

Question 4

(a) (i) An incorrect and incomplete statement of Newton's Second Law of motion is 'Force is proportional to change of momentum'. Write down a correct and complete statement of the law. *(2 marks)*
   (ii) Hence derive an expression in terms of momentum, for the impulse given to a body by a constant force F acting for a time t. *(2 marks)*
   (iii) State **either** the dimensions of impulse **or** the unit of impulse in SI **base** units. *(1 mark)*
   (iv) A tennis player wishing to propel the ball as fast as possible will continue the stroke with the racket (follow through) while striking the ball. Explain, in terms of impulse, why this is done. *(2 marks)*

(b) A tennis player hits a high shot over her opponent. She strikes the ball when it is momentarily stationary and at a height of 1.0 m above the ground, giving it a velocity of 15 m s^{-1} at an angle of 60° above the horizontal.
   (i) The ball, of mass 60 g, is in contact with the racket for 0.30 s. Calculate the impulse given to the ball, and the average force it experiences due to the racket. *(2 marks)*
   (ii) Calculate the values of the horizontal and vertical components of velocity as it leaves the racket. *(2 marks)*
   (iii) Calculate the time taken for the ball to reach a point vertically above the net, which is a horizontal distance of 12.5 m away. Neglect air resistance. *(2 marks)*
   (iv) The player struck the ball when it was at a height of 1.0 m above the ground. Calculate the height above ground at which it crosses the net. *(3 marks)*

(NICCEA)

Question 5

(a) (i) Figure 1.8 shows a view from above of two air-track gliders, A, of mass 0.30 kg, and B, of mass 0.20 kg, travelling towards each other at the speeds shown.

Figure 1.8

0.20 ms⁻¹   0.50 ms⁻¹

A   B

After they collide and separate, A travels with a speed of $0.20 \, \text{m s}^{-1}$ from right to left. Apply the principle of conservation of momentum to this collision, and hence find the velocity of B after the collision.

....

....

....

....

(ii) What general condition must be satisfied for momentum to be conserved in a collision?

....

.... *(5 marks)*

(b) (i) Explain the difference between a *perfectly elastic collision* and an *inelastic collision*.

....

....

(ii) Show that the collision described in part (a) is inelastic.

....

....

....

....

(iii) Give **one** example of perfectly elastic collision.

.... *(3 marks)*

(c) The speed of a bullet can be estimated by firing it horizontally into a block of wood suspended from a long string so that the bullet becomes embedded in the centre of the block. The block swings so that the centre of mass rises a vertical distance of 0.15 m. The mass of the bullet is 10 g and that of the block is 1.99 kg.

(i) Assuming that air resistance can be neglected, calculate the speed of the block and bullet immediately after the impact.

....

....

....

....

(ii) Calculate the speed of the bullet before the impact.

. . . .

. . . .

. . . .

(iii) If the tension in the string just before the impact is T, give **two** reasons why the tension in the string immediately after the impact is greater than T.

. . . .

. . . . (7 marks)

(NEAB)

Question 6

A satellite of mass 100 kg travelling in a circular orbit round the Earth at a height of 300 km above the surface takes 90 minutes to make one complete orbit.

(a) Calculate its angular speed about the centre of the Earth.   (1 mark)

(b) Taking the Earth's radius as 6400 km calculate

    (i) the acceleration of the satellite,

    (ii) the centripetal force acting on it.   (3 marks)

(c) For the satellite in the course of one complete orbit, state and explain what changes, if any, occur to

    (i) the momentum,

    (ii) the kinetic energy.   (4 marks)

(NEAB)

Question 7

An athlete of mass 55 kg runs up a flight of stairs of vertical height 3.6 m in 1.8 s. Calculate the power that this athlete develops in raising his mass.

. . . .

. . . .

. . . .

. . . .

Power = ... (3 marks)

One way of comparing athletes of different sizes is to compare their power-to-weight ratios. Find a unit for the power-to-weight ratio in terms of SI base units.

. . . .

. . . .

. . . .

. . . . (2 marks)

Calculate the athlete's power-to-weight ratio.

. . . .

. . . .

Power-to-weight ratio = ... (2 marks)

(London)

Question 8
This question is about a skateboarder coasting up a ramp.

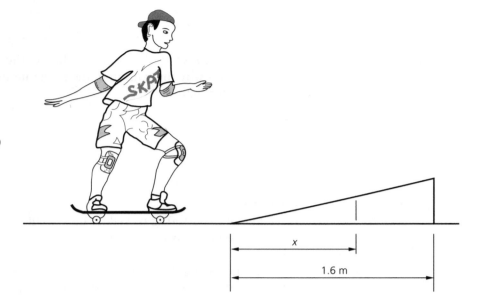

Figure 1.9

A 60 kg skateboarder approaches a ramp, as shown in Fig. 1.9. His speed and horizontal displacement, x, are measured at three places as he coasts up the ramp. These results are used to plot the graph of kinetic energy against x as shown in Fig. 1.10.

Figure 1.10

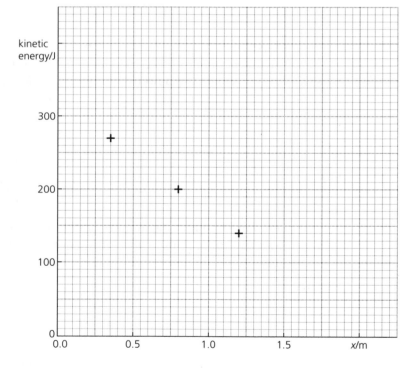

Assume that the skateboarder behaves as a rigid vertical object during the motion.

(a) Make a copy of the graph and then draw a straight line through the points on the graph and deduce, explaining your reasoning:

(i) the kinetic energy of the skateboarder before mounting the ramp;

(1 mark)

(ii) whether the skateboard will reach the top of the ramp.   *(2 marks)*

(b) Suppose, with a different approach speed, the skateboarder just comes to rest at the top of the ramp.
  (i) On the axes of your graph add a second graph, as accurately as you can, of this motion. Label this graph B.   (3 marks)
  (ii) Hence show that the initial speed required for the 60 kg skateboarder to stop at the top of the ramp is about 3 m s^{-1}. (2 marks)
(c) The skateboarder approaches a curved ramp with the same kinetic energy as in (b). Both ramps have the same height.

Figure 1.11

1.6 m

Sketch a third graph to show how kinetic energy may change with x for motion on this ramp. Label this graph C.   (2 marks)
(Nuffield)

Question 9

(a) When a body moves with uniform speed v against a constant resistive force F, the power P dissipated by the resistive force is given by

$$P = Fv.$$

Use base units to show that this equation is dimensionally consistent.
                                                                    (2 marks)
(b) When a certain car of mass 900 kg is moving at a steady speed of 14 m s^{-1} along a level road, the engine provides power to the driving wheels at a rate of 21 kW.
  (i) What is the retarding force on the car?   (2 marks)
  (ii) What power would be needed to drive the car at 14 m s^{-1} up a hill which rises 1 m vertically for every 10 m horizontally?   (4 marks)
  (iii) The car coasts down a slope of a certain gradient at a steady speed of 14 m s^{-1}, without taking any power from the engine. What is the gradient?   (3 marks)
  (iv) In these problems, the calculations (whether they apply to motion on a level road, or to an uphill or downhill slope) have been restricted to a car travelling at one particular speed. Why would it be difficult to solve the problems if the car had been moving at a different speed in each case?

. . . .

. . . .

. . . .

. . . . (2 marks)
(Cambridge)

D.C. circuits, resistance and capacitance

REVISION TIPS

Formulae which you need to be familiar with or to learn. You must be sure which you need to know and which you will be given. Do you know what the symbols represent and can you name the units for each formula?

Current $\qquad I = \dfrac{dQ}{dt}$

Current $\qquad I = nAev$

Resistance $\qquad R = \dfrac{V}{I}$

Resistivity $\qquad \rho = \dfrac{RA}{L}$

Power $\qquad = VI$

Energy $\qquad = VIt$

Charge on a capacitor $\qquad Q = CV$

Resistors in series $\qquad R = R_1 + R_2$

Resistors in parallel $\qquad \dfrac{1}{R} = \dfrac{1}{R_1} + \dfrac{1}{R_2}$

Capacitors in series $\qquad \dfrac{1}{C} = \dfrac{1}{C_1} + \dfrac{1}{C_2}$

The equation for the charge on a discharging capacitor $\qquad Q = Q_0 e^{-t/RC}$

Time constant $\qquad = RC$

Check that you know and understand the following ideas and terminology:
- the relation between current and charge
- what is happening in a conductor when current is flowing
- why a current flowing through a resistor causes a heating effect
- the difference between e.m.f. and p.d.
- the important principles concerning components in series
- the important principles concerning components in parallel
- how the resistance of a wire depends on its length and diameter
- the relation between energy and power
- what the charge on a capacitor depends on
- what is meant by charging and discharging a capacitor and the idea of a time constant
- the exponential nature of the discharge of a capacitor
- why two different capacitors charged in series have the same charge, but in parallel have different charges
- why the energy stored in a capacitor $= \frac{1}{2}QV$.

TOPIC OUTLINE

Current, e.m.f., potential difference and resistance

▶ Current is rate of flow of charge, $I = dQ/dt$: A current of $1\,A = 1\,Cs^{-1}$
▶ Drift velocity $v = I/nAe$, where n is the number of charge carriers per unit volume, e charge, A cross-sectional area. Note that v is greater in semiconductors because n is less (if I and A the same).
▶ E.m.f. E is the electrical energy produced when 1 coulomb of charge passes through a power supply. 1 volt = 1 joule per coulomb
▶ The current in a circuit = $E/total\ resistance$
▶ Potential difference (p.d.) V across a component is the electrical energy converted *to* other forms when 1 coulomb passes through the component.
▶ The resistance R (unit Ω) of a component = V/I
▶ A resistance is *ohmic* if I is proportional to V and hence V/I is constant.

Resistors in series

The same current passes through each resistor. The p.d. across each resistor = IR. The total p.d. across all resistors adds up to the e.m.f. of the power supply (remember to include any internal resistance). The total resistance = sum of all resistances.

Resistors in parallel

The p.d. across each resistor is the same (i.e. IR is the same for each resistor) The total current flowing is the sum of the currents flowing through all the resistors. Use

$$\frac{1}{R_1} + \frac{1}{R_2} = \frac{1}{R}$$

to calculate the total resistance R.

Resistivity

The resistance R of a wire is proportional to its length L, inversely proportional to its cross-sectional area A and depends on the resistivity ρ of the material.

$R = \rho L/A$ Units of $\rho = \Omega$m

Energy and Power

Power = voltage × current, VI is the power dissipated in a component, and EI is the total power delivered by the supply. 'Dissipated' means converted from electrical power to other forms.
Energy = power × time, so energy = VIt, or Eit where t is the time in seconds. As $V = IR$, electrical power converted to heat in a resistor = I^2R and energy = I^2Rt.

Internal resistance

If a power supply has internal resistance r the p.d. V across the terminals of the supply is less than the e.m.f. E by an amount Ir when a current I is flowing.

$V = E - Ir$

i.e. V will get less as I increases. E remains constant.

Tip If a question states that the supply has no internal resistance then this tells you that the p.d. across the terminals of the cell is equal to the e.m.f. no matter what current flows.

A cell of e.m.f. E and internal resistance r connected to an external resistance R will deliver **maximum** power to the external resistor **when $R = r$**.

Power equation is

VI (to external resistor) $= EI$(delivered by cell) $- I^2r$ (wasted in cell)

Kirchhoff's laws

(These should not be revised in isolation, they apply to circuits.)

1 The algebraic sum of the currents at a junction is zero. Basically the total current flowing into a junction = total current flowing out.
2 In a closed loop the sum of the e.m.f.s = the sum of the p.d.s (IR) This is an application of conservation of energy for one coulomb flowing round a circuit. You must take care with signs when adding the e.m.f.s and also when adding the p.d.s.

Balanced potentials

Some circuits are set so that the e.m.f. or p.d. provided by one circuit or part of circuit balances another p.d.

Capacitors

The charge Q on a capacitor is proportional to the p.d. V across the capacitor.

Charge $Q = CV$, where C is the capacitance in farads and V is the p.d. across the capacitor.

Charging a capacitor C through a resistor R

Initially the capacitor is uncharged so there is no p.d. across C and all the battery p.d. is across R. Eventually all the battery p.d. is across C, and there is no p.d. across R. The current in the circuit is always = (p.d. across R)/R, so initially is maximum and finally zero.

Discharging a capacitor C through a resistor R

P.d. across C = p.d. across R leads to the equation

$dQ/dt = -Q/RC$,

which has solution $Q = Q_0e^{-t/RC}$, where Q is charge after time t and Q_0 = initial charge.

This is an exponential decay, because the *rate* of decay of charge is proportional to the charge remaining. Every RC (known as the time constant) seconds the charge (and current) decrease by a factor e. After time RC, $Q = Q_0/e$: after time $2RC$, $Q = Q_0/e^2$

Capacitors in series are charged by the same current for the same time so have the same charge on them, but p.d. across each capacitor = Q/C.

$$\frac{1}{\text{total capacitance}} = \frac{1}{C_1} + \frac{1}{C_2}$$

Capacitors in parallel have the same p.d. across them but the charge on each capacitor = CV.

Total capacitance = $C_1 + C_2$

Energy stored in a capacitor is given by $\frac{1}{2}QV$ or $\frac{1}{2}CV^2$

★ REVISION ACTIVITIES

You should have a copy of the formula sheet provided by your board on your desk.

The following constants may be useful:

$e = 1.6 \times 10^{-19}\,\text{C};\quad L = 6.0 \times 10^{23};\quad$ The atomic mass of copper $= 63\,\text{g}$

The density of copper $= 8900\,\text{kg}\,\text{m}^{-3}$

1   A current of 2 A is flowing a copper wire of diameter 0.8 mm . Calculate:
(a) the cross sectional area A of the wire
(b) the number of 'free' electrons n per unit volume (1 m^3).
(*Hint*. Assume 1 free electron per copper atom and remember 63 g is the mass of 6.0×10^{23} copper atoms.)
(c) the drift velocity of the electrons.

2   A cell of e.m.f. 6.0 V and internal resistance 1.5 Ω is connected to a 3 Ω resistor. Calculate:
(a) the total resistance of the circuit
(b) the current flowing
(c) the p.d. across the cell.

3   Calculate the total resistance of the following combinations of resistors connected in parallel.
(a) 100 Ω and 100 Ω (b) 100 Ω and 1 kΩ (c) 100 Ω and 100 kΩ.

4   Estimate the energy stored in a new 1.5 V cell.

5   Sketch graphs for a capacitor charging through a resistor of:
(a) current against time   (b) charge against time.

6   A 500 μF capacitor is charged to 12 V. Calculate:
(a) the charge on the capacitor
(b) the energy stored in the capacitor.

7   The capacitor in question 6 is now connected across a 4 kΩ resistor. Calculate:
(a) the initial current flowing
(b) the time constant of the circuit
(c) the current after 4 seconds
(d) the charge remaining on the capacitor after 4 seconds
(e) the p.d. across the capacitor after 4 seconds.

? PRACTICE QUESTIONS

Question 1

Figure 2.1 shows two pieces of copper wire of different cross-sectional areas joined together.

The cross-sectional area of piece X is greater than the cross-sectional area of piece Y.

The wires form part of a circuit carrying a constant current. Which of the following statement is (are) correct?

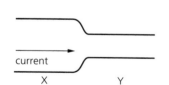

current

X   Y

Figure 2.1

1   The rate of flow of charge through a cross-section of piece Y is greater than the rate of flow of charge through a cross-section of piece X.
2   The drift velocity of the conduction electrons in piece Y is greater than that in piece X.
3   The number of conduction electrons per unit volume in piece Y is greater than that in piece X.

A none of these   **B** 2 only   **C** 3 only   **D** 1 and 2 only   **E** 1 and 3 only

(NICCEA)

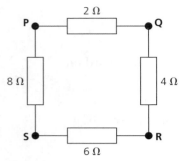

Figure 2.2

Question 2

Four resistors are connected as shown in Fig. 2.2.

Between which two points does the **maximum** resistance of the combination occur?

A P and Q   **B** Q and S   **C** R and S   **D** S and P   **E** P and R

Question 3

A current I flows through a resistance wire of length l, radius r and resistivity ρ.

The wire is replaced by another of length $2l$, radius $2r$ and resistivity 2ρ. What is the magnitude of the current when the applied potential difference is the same?

A $\dfrac{I}{2}$ **B** I **C** $2I$ **D** $4I$ (AEB)

Question 4

This question is about the behaviour of a lamp in a simple circuit.

(a) A student has a lamp which he wishes to light to 'normal brightness'. The rating given on the lamp is '4.5 V, 1.35 W'
   (i) Explain what is meant by a rating of '4.5 V, 1.35 W'.
   (ii) Use this information to calculate the resistance of the lamp filament, under normal operating conditions.   (3 marks)

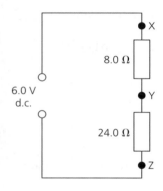

Figure 2.3

The only apparatus available to the student is a 6.0 V d.c. supply, of negligible internal resistance, some resistors, and a digital voltmeter. He connects the circuit shown in Fig. 2.3 with which he intends to produce a voltage difference of 4.5 V across the points YZ.

(b) Explain the reasoning behind this idea.   (2 marks)

(c) To check, he connects the digital voltmeter across YZ and finds that the reading is 4.5 V. He then *disconnects* the voltmeter, and connects the lamp in its place.
   (i) Draw a diagram of the circuit showing the lamp connected as described and explain why the lamp, which is not defective, does not light.
   (ii) He checks the voltage difference across the lamp with the digital voltmeter and finds that the reading is only 1.5 V. Use this fact to show that the resistance of the lamp filament is $3.0\,\Omega$, when connected as described.
   (iii) How do you account for two different values of the resistance of the lamp calculated in part (a)(ii) and part (c)(ii)?   (5 marks)
(Oxford & Cambridge)

Question 5

(a) A battery may be represented by a cell of e.m.f. V in series with an internal resistance r (Fig. 2.4). It is connected to a resistor R. Write down in terms of V, r and R.
   (i) the current in the circuit,

   . . . .   (1 mark)

   (ii) the power dissipated in the resistor R,

   . . . .   (1 mark)

   (iii) the total power dissipated in the circuit.

   . . . .   (1 mark)

   Hence, calculate the proportion of the total power dissipated in the resistor R.

   . . . .

   . . . .   (1 mark)

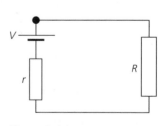

Figure 2.4

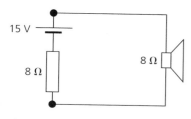

15 V

8 Ω

8 Ω

Figure 2.5

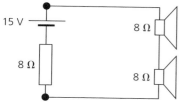

15 V

8 Ω

8 Ω

8 Ω

Figure 2.6

(b) The output of an audio amplifier behaves as an e.m.f. of 15 V in series with an internal resistance of 8 Ω. A student connects an 8 Ω loudspeaker in place of the resistor R (Fig. 2.5). Calculate
(i) the current in the speaker, and

....

.... (1 mark)

(ii) the power dissipated in the speaker.

....

.... (1 mark)

(c) Another student suggests that the amplifier would deliver more power (sound louder) if two 8 Ω loudspeakers were to be used (Fig. 2.6). Calculate the power dissipated in the two speakers combined.

....

....

....

....

....

.... (2 marks)

(d) Compare your calculations in (b) and (c) and comment on them.

....

....

.... (1 mark)
(Oxford & Cambridge)

Question 6
The circuit diagram in Fig. 2.7 shows a cell, of e.m.f. 12 V and internal resistance 0.5 Ω, connected to an external resistor R.
Which one of the following values of the resistance of R will produce a potential difference of 6 V across R?
A 0.1 Ω   **B** 0.5 Ω   **C** 2.0 Ω   **D** 5.0 Ω   (AEB)

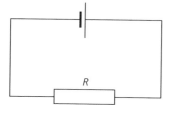

R

Figure 2.7

Questions 7 and 8
Figure 2.8 shows a capacitor C and a resistor R connected in series with a switch S and a battery of negligible internal resistance.

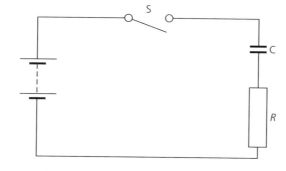

S

C

R

Figure 2.8

Initially, the capacitor is uncharged and the switch is open. Then the switch is closed.

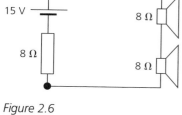

Question 7
Which of the graphs in Fig. 2.9 shows how the current I in the circuit varies
with time t after closing the switch?

Figure 2.9

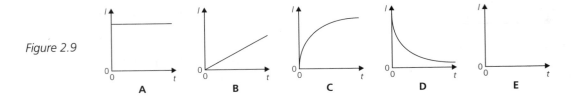

Question 8
Which of the graphs in Fig. 2.10 shows how the total potential difference V
across the combination of capacitor and resistor varies with time t after
closing the switch?

Figure 2.10

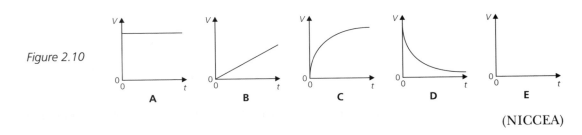

(NICCEA)

Question 9
(a) A capacitor is marked as having a capacitance of $100\,\mu F$. It is also marked
20 V.
   (i) Explain what is meant by 'a capacitance of $100\,\mu F$'.

   . . . .

   . . . .

   . . . .

   (ii) How much charge is stored by the capacitor when a p.d. of 20 V is
        applied across it?

                                      charge = ... C

   (iii) Write down the maximum charge which may safely be stored by the
         capacitor.

                                 maximum charge = ... C

   (iv) Calculate the energy stored by the capacitor when charged as in (ii).

                                      energy = ... J

                                                         (5 marks)

(b) Suggest why the maximum voltage to be used is marked on a capacitor.

   . . . .

   . . . . (1 mark)

(c) The circuit shown in Fig. 2.11 has a 6 V d.c. power supply and is set up with the switch open and the capacitor uncharged.

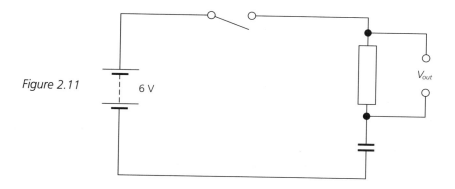

Figure 2.11

The switch is then closed. State what the output voltage V_{out} will be
(i) immediately the switch is closed,
(ii) after a long time.

(2 marks)
(Cambridge)

Question 10
Three capacitors are connected together in the arrangement shown in Fig. 2.12.

Figure 2.12

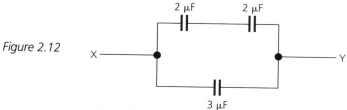

(a) Calculate the total capacitance of this arrangement. *(3 marks)*
(b) (i) State which capacitor stores the greatest amount of charge when a p.d. is applied across XY. Explain your answer.
   (ii) Calculate the value of the charge stored by the capacitor in (i) when the p.d. across XY is 12 V. *(5 marks)*
(NEAB)

3 *Waves and oscillations*

✓ REVISION TIPS

Formulae which you need to be familiar with or to learn. You must be sure which you need to know and which you will be given. Do you know what the symbols represent and can you state the units for each formula?

Simple harmonic motion

Acceleration $a = -\omega^2 x$

Displacement $x = A \cos \omega t$

Velocity $v = -A\omega \sin \omega t$

also $v = \pm \omega \sqrt{A^2 - x^2}$

Period $T = \dfrac{1}{f} = \dfrac{2\pi}{\omega}$

Simple pendulum $T = 2\pi \sqrt{\dfrac{l}{g}}$

Spring-mass system $T = 2\pi \sqrt{\dfrac{m}{k}}$

Waves

Speed $c = f\lambda$

Node-node distance $\dfrac{\lambda}{2}$

Light

Young's slits   Spacing $= \dfrac{D\lambda}{s}$

Diffraction grating $d \sin \theta = n\lambda$

Snell's Law $\dfrac{\sin i}{\sin r} = \dfrac{v_1}{v_2}$

Tackling oscillator problems

- Make sure you fully understand the various sine and cosine graphs which are used. But remember that you may be asked about the $a = -\omega^2 x$ relationship which is *not* a sinusoidal relationship, but instead a straight–line graph with negative slope.
- Check that you can draw graphs of a versus t and v versus t, if given one of x versus t.
- Remember that $\omega = 2\pi f$
- Check that you can do the mechanics to derive a formula for ω in $a = -\omega^2 x$ in a pendulum or a spring-mass system.

Tackling problems in interference and diffraction

▶ Always try to identify the places where constructive and destructive interference occurs.

▶ Remember that *smaller* slit spacings whether in a single, double, or multiple slit system always lead to *larger* patterns.

▶ Check that you really understand the Spacing $= D\lambda/s$ formula and are not confused between the pattern separation distance and the slit separation s.

Refraction and Snell's Law

Students are often confused about Snell's Law, particularly in problems where there are two media of different refractive indices. For light the refractive index n is the ratio of the speed in a vacuum to the speed in the medium, $n = c/v$.

n_{glass}, for example, is $3:2$ and light which travels at $3 \times 10^8 \, \mathrm{m \, s^{-1}}$ in a vacuum travels at $2 \times 10^8 \, \mathrm{m \, s^{-1}}$ in glass, and $n_{water} = 4:3$ and light travels at $2.25 \times 10^8 \, \mathrm{m \, s^{-1}}$ in water. Glass has a higher refractive index than water and is said to be **optically denser** than water. Light slows down and bends towards the normal on entering a denser medium, and bends away from the normal when leaving a denser medium. As the frequency of the wave does not change the ratio of the wavelength in a vacuum to the wavelength in the medium is also the refractive index.

Figure 3.1 shows a ray travelling from glass to water. In one of its forms Snell's Law states that the product $n \sin i$ is a constant.

Hence $n_g \sin i_g = n_w \sin i_w$

and remember that $n_{air} = 1$.

The critical angle phenomenon is then shown by Fig. 3.2.

Here $n_1 \sin c = n_2 \sin 90°$, so

$$\sin c = n_2/n_1,$$

and at angles greater than the critical angle total internal reflection occurs.

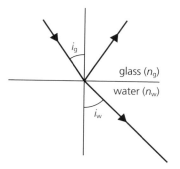

Figure 3.1
Ray travelling from glass to water

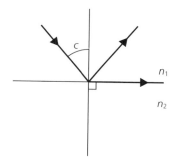

Figure 3.2
Critical angle

Figure 3.3
Total internal reflection

TOPIC OUTLINE

An oscillation is any repeated cycle of motion about an equilibrium position (but note that the idea extends to electrical oscillations where a p.d., charge, or current varies cyclically about an equilibrium value). **Simple Harmonic Motion** is a special class of oscillation where the period, T, or the time for a complete cycle of the oscillation, is the same for all amplitudes be they large or small. If and only if an oscillator has this property then it follows that:

1 The oscillation is sinusoidal.
2 The acceleration is proportional to the magnitude of the displacement x from the equilibrium position but directed always towards the equilibrium position, that is the mid-point of the motion. This condition is summarised by the equation $a = -\omega^2 x$. Note that ω^2 is usually found by analysing the forces operating.

The period T is then given by $T = 2\pi/\omega$. The frequency f is $1/T$ and the following sinusoidal equations usually represent the displacement and velocity of the simple harmonic oscillator where the oscillator is released from an extreme position A, the amplitude of the motion at $t = 0$:

$$x = A \cos \omega t \qquad v = -A\omega \sin \omega t$$

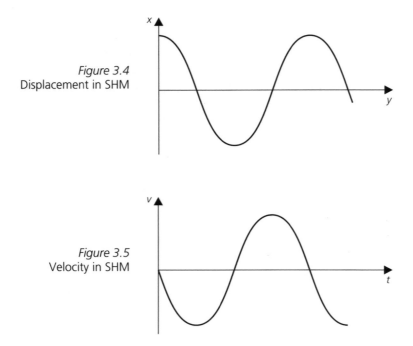

Figure 3.4
Displacement in SHM

Figure 3.5
Velocity in SHM

(Note, however, that some books choose a different point in the cycle for the zero of time. For example if $x = A \sin \omega t$, then $v = A\omega \cos \omega t$.)

Most real oscillators are damped, i.e. there is a steady loss of energy, usually through friction but also by wave motion (e.g. a vibrating tuning fork loses energy by generating sound waves.) When the damping forces are proportional to the velocity, v, the period remains constant as the amplitude diminishes. Unless the damping is considerable the frequency is not appreciably different from what it would be without any damping. But with heavier damping, and beyond an important condition called **critical damping**, there are no oscillations and the displacement exponentially diminishes to zero. A critically-damped oscillator is one where the time constant of the exponential decay takes the minimum value it can have.

Frequently a periodic force is applied to an oscillator causing a **forced** as distinct to a **free** vibration, e.g. the vibrations of a motor in a spin dryer applied to the casing. Initially the system exhibits 'transient' behaviour and then settles down with oscillations at the frequency of the driving force. When the driving frequency is at the same frequency as the natural frequency of the oscillator the amplitude of oscillation is at its greatest. This is called **resonance** and for a simple harmonic oscillator there will only be one frequency of resonance.

Stationary or standing waves

These are more complicated examples of resonance and can occur at several different frequencies. Guitar strings provide a good example. A typical sequence in time is shown.

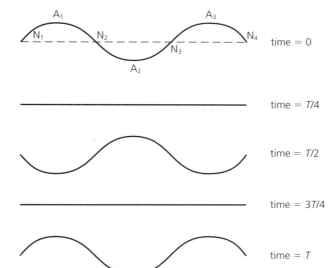

Figure 3.6
'Snapshots' of a
standing wave system

Points of maximum amplitude, A_1, A_2, A_3, are called **antinodes** and points of no motion, N_1, N_2, N_3, N_4 are **nodes**. The distance between adjacent nodes is $\lambda/2$

i.e. $N_1 N_2 = A_1 A_2 = \dfrac{\lambda}{2}$ where λ is the wavelength.

Standing waves are also understood as the **superposition** (or adding up) of two **travelling waves** of the same frequency and wavelength, but travelling in opposite directions, and simultaneously present in the medium.

Travelling waves can be classified as **transverse** or **longitudinal**. When such waves are sinusoidal in profile the oscillations of individual particles or elements of the medium are simple harmonic. When these local oscillations are perpendicular to the direction in which the wave travels, the wave is called transverse. Ripples on water and electromagnetic waves are of this kind. When the oscillations take place to and fro along the direction the wave travels the waves are called longitudinal. Sound is an example.

All wave systems can show the properties of **reflection**, **refraction**, **interference** and **diffraction**. Transverse waves can also show **polarisation**. Waves obey the equation $c = f\lambda$, where λ is the wavelength and f the frequency; c is then the speed and is usually independent of the wavelength. In some cases such as light in a glass block, the speed depends on the wavelength, and the medium is said to be dispersive.

Interference patterns from two sources can be produced, provided that the sources are coherent, i.e. they are in phase with each other, or there is a constant difference of phase. The classic pattern studied at A-Level is that of Young's slits. In its general form there are two sources, a distance s apart.

Constructive interference occurs at every point on the screen where the path difference to the two sources (slits) is equal to a whole number of wavelengths. Destructive interference, where the waves cancel each other occurs when the path difference is a whole number of wavelengths plus a half wavelength. The separation S of points of constructive interference is given by the formula

$S = D\lambda/s.$

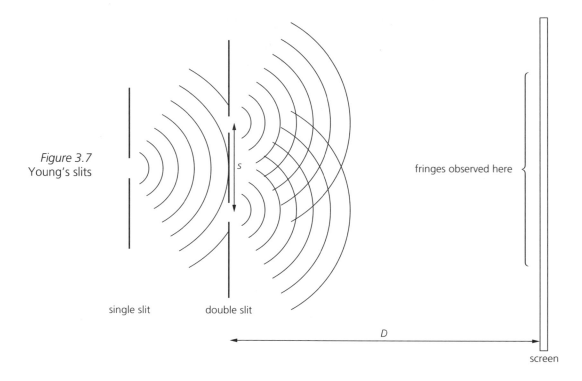

Figure 3.7
Young's slits

Coherence in the light at the two slits is achieved by using the **diffraction**, or spreading out, of waves from a single slit which reach the two slits so that they radiate light with a constant phase difference.

A **diffraction grating** uses interference of diffracted light from a large number of regularly spaced slits. When the slit separation is d constructive interference occurs at angles θ given by $d \sin \theta = n\lambda$ where n is 0, 1, 2, 3 etc.

When there is a change in the medium carrying a wave, for example in its density, both the speed and wavelength, but not the frequency, change. Unless the **wavefronts** are parallel to the boundary associated with the change, there is a change of direction called **refraction**, and described by Snell's Law: $\sin i / \sin r = v_1 / v_2$. (see Revision Tips) The ratio of the two speeds v_1 / v_2 is called the refractive index n. **Total internal reflection** can occur when there is a change in the medium with the wave speeding up. If the wave strikes the interface at an angle greater than the critical angle, c, given by $n = 1 / \sin c$, it is reflected backwards rather than refracted in the forward direction.

REVISION ACTIVITIES

Check that you can do the following:

1 Define the following in words and, where appropriate, using a formula: oscillation, period, frequency, amplitude, SHM, forced oscillation, critical damping.
2 Write down formulae for displacement, velocity, acceleration, period and frequency for a spring-mass system.
3 Draw standing waves diagrams for a transverse standing wave at $t = 0$, $t = T/4$, $t = T/2$, $t = 3T/4$ and $t = T$. Mark the nodes and antinodes.
4 Repeat the above for a longitudinal wave system.
5 Look up and describe the term polarisation.
6 Look up the experimental details of a Young's slits arrangement in optics. Draw a schematic diagram, and draw the likely fringe pattern.

7 Explain the terms wavefront, normal, wavelength, reflection, refraction and refractive index, using the two diagrams below.

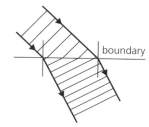

Figure 3.8
Plane waves (and rays) reflecting from a plane surface

Figure 3.9
Refraction of a plane wave

PRACTICE QUESTIONS

Question 1

The diagrams show two identical masses, which can oscillate on different combinations of identical springs.

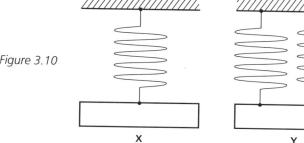

Figure 3.10

The approximate ratio of natural frequencies of the systems $f_X : f_Y$ is
A $1:2$ **B** $1:1.4$ **C** $1:0.7$ **D** $1:0.5$ (AEB)

Question 2

Which graph shows the relationship between the acceleration a and the displacement x of a particle performing simple harmonic motion?

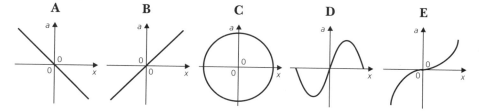

Figure 3.11

Question 3

A particle of mass m executes simple harmonic motion in a straight line of amplitude a and frequency f. Which of the following expressions represents the total energy of the particle?
A $2\pi^2 mfa^2$ **B** $2\pi^2 mf^2 a^2$ **C** $4\pi^2 m^2 f^2 a$ **D** $4\pi^2 mf^2 a^2$
(AEB – specimen question)

Question 4

A body oscillates with simple harmonic motion. On the axes in Fig. 3.12 sketch a graph to show how the acceleration of the body varies with its displacement.
(2 marks)

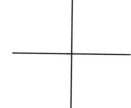

Figure 3.12

How could the graph be used to determine T, the period of oscillation of the body?

....

....

....

.... *(2 marks)*

A displacement-time graph for simple harmonic motion is drawn below.

Figure 3.13

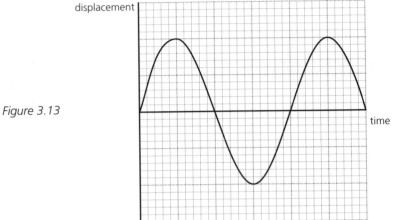

The movement of tides can be regarded as simple harmonic, with a period of approximately 12 hours.

On a uniformly sloping beach, the distance along the sand between the high water mark and the low water mark is 50 m. A family builds a sand castle 10 m below the high water mark while the tide is on its way out. Low tide is at 2.00 p.m.

On the graph

(i) label points L and H, showing the displacements at low tide and the next high tide,

(ii) draw a line parallel to the time axis showing the location of the sand castle,

(iii) add the times of low and high tide.   *(3 marks)*

Calculate the time at which the rising tide reaches the sand castle.

....

....

....

....

Time = ... *(3 marks)*

(London)

Question 5

(a) State the conditions for a body to undergo simple harmonic motion.

(b) The diagram shows how the displacement of a body undergoing simple harmonic oscillations varies with time.

Figure 3.14

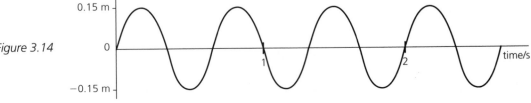

(i) Determine the frequency and amplitude of the oscillations.
(ii) Determine the maximum acceleration of the body.
(iii) Copy the diagram and draw labelled graphs **with the same time scale** to show the corresponding variations of velocity and acceleration.

(8 marks)

(AEB)

Question 6

Figure 3.15 shows a standing wave pattern of a steel guitar string stretched between two supports, called the nut and the bridge, on a guitar.

The fundamental standing wave pattern shown produces a note of frequency 280 Hz.

Figure 3.15

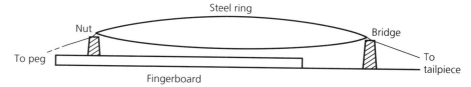

(a) By placing a finger **lightly** at certain places on the string it is possible to produce further standing wave patterns with other specific frequencies.
(i) Sketch on Fig. 3.15 one of these standing wave patterns, and
(ii) state its frequency.

(2 marks)

(b) The speed, c, of a transverse wave along a stretched string is given by

$c = \sqrt{\dfrac{T}{\mu}}$, where T is the tension and μ the mass per unit length of the string.

Show that the fundamental frequency f is given by $f = \dfrac{1}{2l}\sqrt{\dfrac{T}{\mu}}$, where l is the vibrating length of the string between nut and bridge. *(2 marks)*

(c) Assuming that both l and μ remained constant, calculate the frequency of the new fundamental mode of vibration if the tension were halved.

(2 marks)

(d) In practice μ, the mass per unit length, changes because the string contracts when the tension is reduced.
Consider a situation in which the tension is halved.
(i) If the strain reduction produced were 0.4% what would be the percentage change in μ? State both the size and sign of the change.

(3 marks)

(ii) Write down the percentage error this would cause in your answer to (c). State, giving your reasoning, whether the actual frequency would be higher or lower than that you calculated. *(2 marks)*

(Nuffield)

Question 7

A student was studying the motion of a simple pendulum the time period of which was given by $T = 2\pi(l/g)^{1/2}$.
He measured T for values of l given by

$l/m = 0.10, 0.40, 0.70, 1.00$

and plotted a graph of T against $\sqrt{l}$ in order to deduce a value for g, the free-fall acceleration. Explain why these values for l are poorly chosen.

. . . .

. . . . *(1 mark)*

How would the student obtain a value of *g* from the gradient of the graph?

. . . .

. . . .

. . . .

. . . . *(2 marks)*

The graph below shows three cycles of oscillation for an undamped pendulum of length 1.00 m.

Figure 3.16

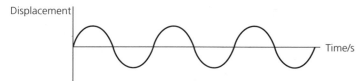

Add magnitudes to the time axis and on the same axes show three cycles for the same pendulum when its motion is lightly air damped.   *(4 marks)*

                                                           (London)

Question 8

The diagram shows the displacement-time graphs for two waveforms.

Figure 3.17

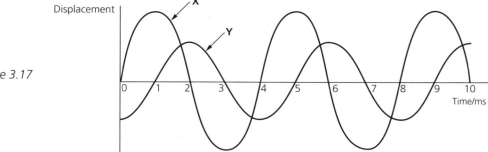

What is the phase difference between the two waveforms **X** and **Y**?

A 1 ms with **X** leading.   **C** $\pi/2$ radians with **X** leading.
B 1 ms with **Y** leading.   **D** $\pi/2$ radians with **Y** leading.   (AEB)

Question 9

A progressive wave moves along a stretched spring. Figure 3.18 shows the variation of displacement with distance along the spring at one instant.

Figure 3.18

(a) Copy Fig. 3.18 and indicate on it:
    (i) the amplitude of the wave;
    (ii) the wavelength.   *(2 marks)*
(b) (i) Why does a stretched string which has both ends fixed produce
         stationary waves when it is plucked?   *(2 marks)*

(ii) Sketch a diagram to illustrate the third harmonic vibrations of a stretched string for a fixed length and tension. *(2 marks)*

(iii) State and explain the relation between the frequencies of the first and second harmonics. *(3 marks)*

(AEB)

Question 10

Figure 3.19

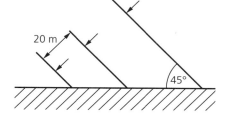

The graph shows, at a particular instant, the variation of the displacement of the particles in a transverse progressive water wave, of wavelength 4 cm, travelling from left to right. Which one of the following statements is not true?

A The distance PS = 3 cm.

B The particle velocity at Q is a maximum.

C Particles at P and R are in phase.

D The particle at S is moving downwards. (AEB)

Question 11

The metre was defined in terms of the wavelength λ of the orange spectral line emitted by excited atoms of Krypton-86. Thus 1 metre = $n\lambda$ where n is the number of wavelengths in 1 metre of vacuum.

What is the best value for n?

A 1.65×10^6 **B** 1.43×10^4 **C** 3.00×10^8 **D** 2.00×10^8 **E** 3.33×10^{12}

Question 12

Parallel water waves of wavelength 20 m strike a straight sea wall. The wavefronts make an angle of 45° with the wall as shown.

Figure 3.20

What is the difference in phase at any instant between the waves at two points 10 m apart along the wall?

A 45°   **B** 90°   **C** 180°   **D** 360°   **E** 127°

Question 13

In a 'radar' speed measuring device, a transmitter emitting a radio wave of wavelength 30 mm is placed alongside a receiver as shown in Fig. 3.21. Some of the output of the transmitter is fed (by the wire shown) directly to the receiver, and is then compared with the reflected signal.

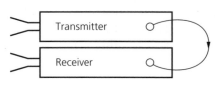

Figure 3.21

M

(a) A sheet of metal, M, is held in front of the device as shown, so that the intensity detected by the receiver is a maximum.
When the metal sheet is moved 7.5 mm towards the device the intensity falls to a minimum. Explain, in words, why
  (i) the receiver signal decreases,
  (ii) the minimum is not necessarily zero.   (*3 marks*)
(b) The radiation is now directed at an approaching motor-car which is moving directly towards the device at a steady speed, and the receiver detects a signal fluctuating in strength with a frequency of 2.0 kHz.
Calculate the speed of the car.   (*3 marks*)
(c) When the car, of mass 1200 kg, has travelled a distance of 100 m in a straight line towards the device the observed frequency is found to be 1.0 kHz.
Calculate the average braking force applied, stating any assumptions made.   (*3 marks*)
(Nuffield)

Question 14
Figure 3.22 shows a string with its ends P and Q fixed. A transverse stationary wave is set up in the string so that P, Q and the mid-point R are the only points on the string which are nodes.

Figure 3.22

P   S   R   T   Q

The points S and T are equidistant from the mid-point R. Which of the following describes the vibrations of S and T?
A They have the same amplitude and are in phase.
B They have different amplitudes and are in phase.
C They have the same amplitude and differ in phase by 90°.
D They have the same amplitude and differ in phase by 180°.
E They have different amplitudes and differ in phase by 180°.   (NICCEA)

Question 15
The diagram shows two identical loudspeakers driven in phase from a common audio-frequency source.

Figure 3.23

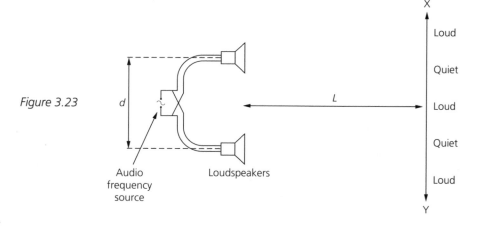

When a student moves along a line such as XY he notices that there are regions in which the sound heard is alternately loud and quiet. Regions in which the sound is loud may be moved closer together by
A decreasing distance *d*
B increasing distance *L*
C increasing the frequency of the audio-frequency source
D increasing the power output from the audio-frequency source   (AEB)

Question 16
Figure 3.24 shows a horizontal rectangular tank containing water. A plane mirror is placed at an angle to the bottom surface of the tank.

Figure 3.24

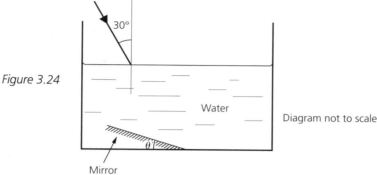

A ray of light is incident on the surface of the water an at angle of 30° as shown.
(a) For small values of the angle θ the ray is reflected from the surface of the mirror and emerges at a point on the surface of the water. Redraw the diagram in your answer book and show the path of the ray of light through the liquid and after it has emerged from the water surface.

(3 marks)

(b) Using the data below calculate
   (i) the angle of refraction for the ray as it enters the water,
   (ii) the critical angle at a water air boundary.   *(3 marks)*
(c) For a particular value of the angle θ, the reflected ray is incident on the water surface at the critical angle.
   Calculate this angle θ.
   Refractive index of water = 1.33   *(2 marks)*
                                                          (NEAB)

Radioactivity and photoelectric effect

✓ REVISION TIPS

Formulae which you need to be familiar with or to learn . You must be sure which you need to know and which you will be given. Do you know what the symbols represent and can you name the units for each formula?

Activity	$\dfrac{dN}{dt} = -\lambda N$
Decay constant	$\lambda = \dfrac{\ln 2}{t_{\frac{1}{2}}}$
Energy change	$\Delta E = \Delta mc^2$
Energy of a photon	$E = hf$
Einstein's equation	$\frac{1}{2} mv^2_{\max} = hf - \varphi$
De Broglie equation	$mv = \dfrac{h}{\lambda}$

Check that you *know* and *understand* the following ideas and terminology:

▶ proton number, nucleon number, nuclide, isotope, ionisation
▶ the main evidence for the nuclear model of the atom (Rutherford's Experiment)
▶ the nature, and means of detection,of alpha, beta and gamma radiation and the effect on the nucleus of the emission of alpha and beta particles
▶ the randomness of radioactive decay, activity of a source, decay constant λ, half life $t_{\frac{1}{2}}$
▶ the applications of the equations $dN/dt = -\lambda N$ and $\lambda = \ln 2/t_{\frac{1}{2}}$
▶ how to calculate the power available from a radioactive source
▶ the meaning of the terms mass defect, binding energy and the significance of the equation $\Delta E = \Delta mc^2$ and the principle of the release of energy by the process of nuclear fission and fusion
▶ what is meant by a photon and the photoelectric effect
▶ that Einstein's photoelectric equation $\frac{1}{2}(mv^2)_{\max} = hf - \varphi$ is an expression of conservation of energy
▶ wave/particle duality, and that for a particle wavelength $\lambda = h/mv$

◎ TOPIC OUTLINE

▶ **Atom** $\sim 10^{-10}$ m diameter: consists of nucleus + orbiting electrons.
▶ **Nucleus** $\sim 10^{-14}$ m diameter: contains protons and neutrons.
▶ **Electron**: charge $e = -1.6 \times 10^{-19}$ C: mass $m_e = 9.1 \times 10^{-31}$ kg. (You will be given these values.)
▶ **Proton**: particle with charge $= +1.6 \times 10^{-19}$ C: mass $m_p \sim 1800\, m_e$.

▶ **Neutron**: uncharged: mass $\sim m_p$.
▶ **Nucleon**: neutron or proton.
▶ **Nucleon (mass) number** A: total number of neutrons and protons.
▶ **Proton (atomic) number** Z: number of protons, determines which element.
▶ **Nuclide** $_Z^A\text{X}$: Isotope, same number of protons(same element), different number of neutrons, i.e. same Z, different A
▶ **Neutral atom**: overall uncharged: same number of electrons as protons.
▶ **Ionisation**: process of removal of electron from an atom, creating a positive ion and an electron, known as an ion pair.
  1 eV: the energy gained by 1 electron accelerated by 1 volt:
  $1\,\text{eV} = 1.6 \times 10^{-19}\,\text{J}$
  (This is because the charge on 1 electron $= 1.6 \times 10^{-19}\,\text{C}$)
  $1\,\text{MeV} = 1.6 \times 10^{-13}\,\text{J}$
▶ **Alpha, α**: a particle spontaneously ejected from nuclei of certain isotopes: energy a few MeV: range in air a few cm, depending on k.e., alpha consists of 2 protons and 2 neutrons. Hence nucleon number A of nucleus emitting an alpha particle decreases by 4 and the proton number Z decreases by 2.
▶ **Beta particle**: an electron spontaneously ejected from the nuclei of certain atoms. A is unchanged and Z *increases* by 1. Essentially neutron changes into proton and anti-neutrino, which takes some of the energy. Maximum range of beta in air $\sim 30\,\text{cm}$.
▶ **Gamma radiation**: electromagnetic radiation of very short wavelength ($\sim 10^{-11}\,\text{m}$): energy a few MeV.
▶ α, β and γ radiation all cause ionisation. α and β particles lose k.e. as they ionise the surroundings. The α eventually picks up two electrons to become a helium atom.
▶ **Rutherford's Experiment**
  – **Experiment**: Alpha particles fired at thin gold foil.
  – **Results**: Most went straight through; about 1 in 8000 were deflected more than 90°.
  – **Conclusion**: Thompson plum pudding model replaced by model of small positively charged nucleus surrounded by orbiting electrons. Detailed calculation on deflections of alphas showed that force, acting on the alphas, obeyed inverse square law.

  Can you sketch the path of an alpha passing near to a gold nucleus?

  – The smaller the aiming error, the nearer the alpha approaches the nucleus.
  – The alpha loses k.e. as it gains electrical p.e. getting nearer to the nucleus.
  – Head on collision: closest approach r: equate k.e. of α to p.e. $Q_1 Q_2 / 4\pi\varepsilon_0 r$, where Q_1 is the charge on $\alpha = 4e$, Q_2 is the charge on gold nucleus $= 79e$.

Radioactive decay

▶ The emission of an alpha or a beta particle from a source implies that the atom has decayed (the proton number of the nucleus has changed).
▶ **Activity**: number of atoms decaying per second . Obviously the activity is also the number of particles emitted per second. The unit is 1 becquerel (Bq) = 1 decay per second.
▶ The half life $t_{\frac{1}{2}}$ is the time taken for the number of atoms *or* the activity to halve. After two half-lives the number of atoms and the activity has quartered and so on.
▶ Radioactive decay is a random process. Each atom has a fixed chance λ of decay per second. λ is known as the decay constant. Bigger λ, smaller $t_{\frac{1}{2}}$: $\lambda = \ln 2 / t_{\frac{1}{2}}$
▶ The activity $dN/dt = -\lambda N = -N\ln 2 / t_{\frac{1}{2}}$: depends on $t_{\frac{1}{2}}$ and N, the number of atoms remaining.

HINT

To calculate N,
if Z = 256 or atomic
mass = 256 g then 256 g
contains 6×10^{23} atoms.

The solution to this equation is $N = N_0 e^{-\lambda t}$, where N is the number of atoms remaining after time t and N_0 is the number at $t = 0$.

Also $dN/dt = (dN_0/dt)e^{-\lambda t}$

Power available from a radioactive source = activity × energy of each particle.

Binding energy

The nucleons in a nucleus must be *given* energy to separate them into separate neutrons and protons. Hence when they are held together in the nucleus they have less energy, the difference being the binding energy. When they are separate they have zero energy and so the binding energy is negative. The graph of binding energy *per nucleon* against nucleon number reaches a maximum binding energy at a nucleon number ~50. This explains why two lighter nuclei will release energy if **fused** together at high speed and why a heavier nucleus will release energy if **fissioned** (split into two parts) by bombarding it with thermal neutrons.

$\Delta E = \Delta mc^2$

ΔE = change in energy, Δm = change in mass, c speed of light. This equation implies that when particles have less energy they have less mass. When the nucleons are collected in the nucleus they have less energy and less mass, known as the **mass defect**. The equation can be used to calculate the binding energy knowing the mass defect.

Wave/particle duality

Light, radio, X rays, gamma rays and all electromagnetic radiations are treated as wave motions for the consideration of the effects of reflection, refraction, interference and diffraction. For other effects such as the photoelectric effect, they are treated as though they consist of particles, packets of energy or photons. Energy of photon $= hf$, where h is the Planck Constant and f is the frequency of the radiation. The corresponding wavelength $\lambda = c/f$, where c is the speed of light.

Particles, such as electrons, exhibit wave effects such as interference and diffraction. Hence they have a wavelength which is given by De Broglie's equation $mv = h/\lambda$ (The equation $c = f\lambda$ does *not* apply to these matter waves.)

Photoelectric effect

Light incident on a metal surface releases electrons if the energy hf of a photon is bigger than the work function φ (least energy to release an electron) of the metal. i.e. $hf > \varphi$

The **maximum** kinetic energy of released electrons $= \frac{1}{2}mv_{max}^2 = hf - \varphi$

Compare to $y = mx + c$. Plot $\frac{1}{2}mv_{max}^2$ against f; the gradient $= h$ and the y-intercept $= -\varphi$.

The x-intercept $= f_0$, called the **threshold frequency**, is the smallest frequency which will release photoelectrons from this metal surface.

$hf_0 = \varphi$

If f is fixed, increasing the brightness increases the number of photons, releasing more electrons. Increasing f increases the energy of each photon and hence increases $\frac{1}{2}mv_{max}^2$.

If the released electrons are stopped by a p.d. V then electrical energy gained = k.e. lost.

$eV_{max} = \frac{1}{2}mv_{max}^2$ and, from above equation, $eV_{max} = hf - \varphi$. Note that V_{max} can be plotted against f.

Emission spectra and energy levels

The orbital electrons in an atom are allowed only certain discrete amounts of energy. These amounts of energy are represented by energy levels.

An atom emits photons electromagnetic radiation when an electron falls from a higher level energy E_2 to a lower level energy E_1. The energy hf of the photon emitted $= E_2 - E_1$.

The corresponding wavelength $\lambda = c/f$, where c is the speed of light. Hence each atom emits only certain wavelengths, called the **emission spectrum**, characteristic of its energy levels.

REVISION ACTIVITIES

You should have a copy of the formula sheet provided by your board on your desk.

The following constants may be useful.

$e = 1.6 \times 10^{-19}\,\mathrm{C}$ 　　　 $L = 6.0 \times 10^{23}$ 　　　 1 year $= 3 \times 10^7\,\mathrm{s}$
$h = 6.63 \times 10^{-34}\,\mathrm{Js}^{-1}$ 　 $c = 3 \times 10^8\,\mathrm{m\,s}^{-1}$ 　　 $m_e = 9.1 \times 10^{-31}\,\mathrm{kg}$

1 Write down all the formulae which you need to *know* in this section of the syllabus.

2 Calculate the number of atoms in 1 kg of $^{235}\mathrm{U}$.

3 Calculate the maximum power available from a radioactive source emitting α particles of energy 5 MeV, if the activity of the source $= 120\,\mathrm{Bq}$.

4 Calculate the decay constant for a source whose half-life is 1500 yrs.

5 Which of the following two sources will have the greater activity?
　A 100 g of $^{90}\mathrm{Sr}$ whose half-life is 25 yrs
　B 100 g of $^{60}\mathrm{Co}$ whose half-life is 5 yrs

6 Calculate the energy of a photon of yellow light of wavelength 600 nm.

7 How many photons of light does a 100 W bulb emit? (Assume yellow light for wavelength.)

8 Calculate the wavelength associated with an electron travelling at $6 \times 10^6\,\mathrm{m\,s}^{-1}$.

PRACTICE QUESTIONS

Question 1

The half-life of a certain radioactive nuclide is 20 hours. Initially, the activity of a sample of this nuclide is 100 Bq. What is the activity after 5 hours?

　A 84 Bq 　　 **B** 75 Bq 　　 **C** 50 Bq 　　 **D** 25 Bq 　　 **E** 16 Bq 　　　　(NICCEA)

Question 2

A radioactive nucleus X decays by a series of disintegrations, involving the emission of a total of three alpha-particles and two beta-particles, to a stable isotope of lead, which has atomic number 82 and mass number 207. What are the values of the atomic number and the mass number of X?

	Atomic number	Mass number
A	86	213
B	86	219
C	90	219
D	94	211
E	94	215

　　　　　　　　　　　　　　　　　　　　　　　　　　　　　　(NICCEA)

Question 3

The activity of a piece of radioactive material is 4.3×10^5 Bq at time $t = 0$.
The number of undecayed atoms in the material at time $t = 0$ is 7.9×10^{15}.
Calculate

(a) (i) the activity after 4.0 half-lives have elapsed,

     (ii) the number of undecayed atoms after 4.0 half-lives,   *(4 marks)*

(b) the decay constant λ,   *(3 marks)*

(c) the half-life $t_{\frac{1}{2}}$.   *(2 marks)*

                                                           (Cambridge)

Question 4

In an experiment, a ratemeter was held a fixed distance from a sample of
radioactive material. The readings taken from the ratemeter have been used
to plot the graph, Fig. 4.1, of the count rate C against the time t.

Fig. 4.1

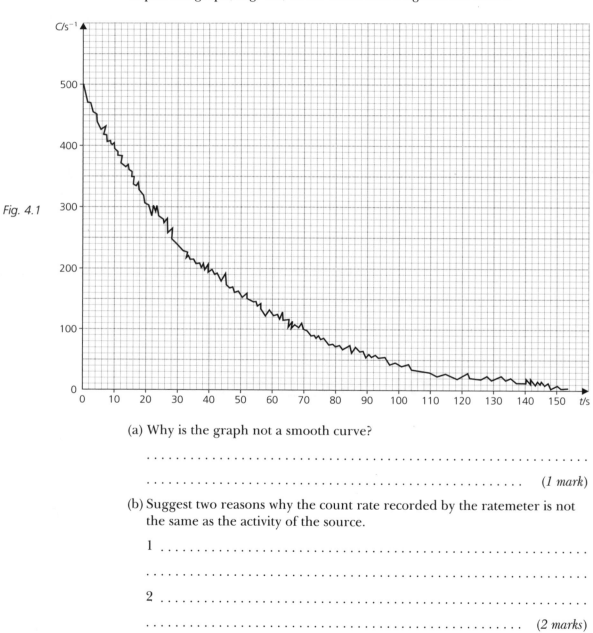

(a) Why is the graph not a smooth curve?

. . . .

. . . . *(1 mark)*

(b) Suggest two reasons why the count rate recorded by the ratemeter is not
the same as the activity of the source.

    1 . . . .

. . . .

    2 . . . .

. . . . *(2 marks)*

(c) On Fig. 4.1, draw the smooth curve of best-fit, and use your curve to find
the half-life of the radioactive material.

                                half-life = ... s *(4 marks)*

                                                                (Cambridge)

Question 5

An α-source with an activity of 150 kBq is placed in a metal can as shown. A 100 V d.c. source and a 10^9 Ω resistor are connected in series to the can and the source. This arrangement, shown in Fig. 4.2, is sometimes called an ionisation chamber.

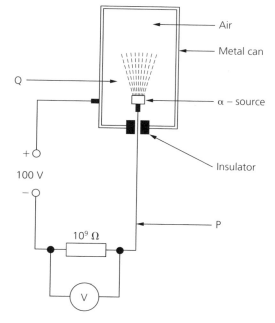

Figure 4.2

(a) What is meant in this case by *an activity of 150 kBq*? (2 marks)

(b) Describe how the nature of the electric current in the wire at P differs from that in the air at Q. (3 marks)

(c) A potential difference of 3.4 V is registered on the voltmeter.
   (i) Calculate the current in the wire at P. State any assumption you make.
   (ii) Calculate the corresponding number of ionisations occurring in the metal can every second. State any assumption you make. (5 marks)

(d) With the α-source removed from the metal can, the voltmeter still registers a potential difference of 0.2 V. Suggest two reasons why the current is not zero. (2 marks)

(e) The half-life of the α-source is known to be 1600 years. Calculate the decay constant and hence deduce the number of radioactive atoms in the source. (4 marks)

(London)

Question 6

Figure 4.3 shows some of the outer energy levels of the mercury atom.

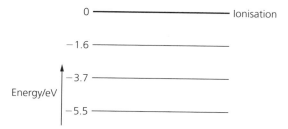

Figure 4.3

Calculate the ionisation energy in joules for an electron in the $-10.4\,\text{eV}$ level.

. . . .

. . . .

Ionisation energy = ...   (*2 marks*)

An electron has been excited to the $-1.6\,\text{eV}$ energy level. Show on the diagram all the possible ways it can return to the $-10.4\,\text{eV}$ level.   (*3 marks*)

Which change in energy levels will give rise to a yellowish line ($\lambda \approx 600\,\text{nm}$) in the mercury spectrum?

. . . .

. . . .

. . . .

. . . .

. . . .

. . . .   (*4 marks*)

(London)

Questions **7** and **8** are about experiments on the photoelectric effect, using an evacuated photocell with a pure metal cathode. The cathode is illuminated with light of a single, fixed wavelength. The photoelectrons emitted have a spread of values of kinetic energy, up to a definite maximum value. The intensity of the light can be varied.

Question 7
Which of the graphs in Fig. 4.4 shows the way in which the photoelectric current depends on the intensity of the light?

Figure 4.4

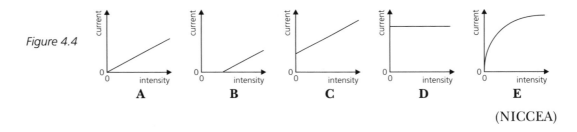

(NICCEA)

Question 8
Which of the graphs in Fig. 4.5 shows the way in which the maximum value of the kinetic energy of the photoelectrons depends on the intensity of the light?

Figure 4.5

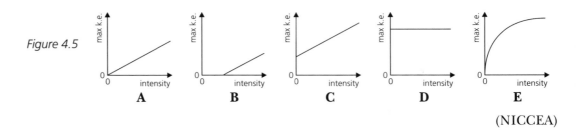

(NICCEA)

Question 9

Which of the following graphs in Fig. 4.6 best represents the way in which the energy E of a photon of light depends on the wavelength λ of the light?

Figure 4.6

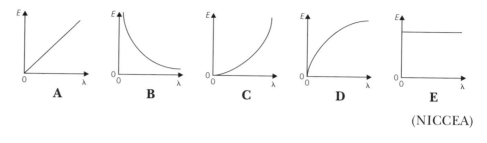

A   B   C   D   E

(NICCEA)

Question 10

Monochromatic light of wavelength 450 nm falls on the cathode of a photocell at a rate of 25 μW. Only 10% of the photons produce an electron and all these electrons produce a current, I, in an external circuit.
The following data is needed in this question.

the Planck constant $= 6.63 \times 10^{-34}$ J s
speed of light in vacuo $= 3.00 \times 10^{8}$ m s^{-1}
charge of an electron $= -1.60 \times 10^{-19}$ C

(a) Calculate

(i) the energy of one photon in J,

. . . .

. . . .

. . . .

. . . .

(ii) the number of photons falling on the cathode per second,

. . . .

. . . .

. . . .

. . . .

(iii) the current, I.

. . . .

. . . .

. . . . (4 marks)

(b) The same amount of energy per second falls on the cathode in the form of light of wavelength 600 nm.
The work function of the material of the cathode is 3.0×10^{-19} J.
Show that a photoelectric current will flow.

. . . .

. . . .

. . . .

. . . . (2 marks)

(NEAB)

Question 11

This question is about a nuclear reactor used to power a submarine.

(a) In a nuclear reactor the process of nuclear fission is caused by neutron bombardment. The following equation summarises what may happen:

$$^{235}U + {}^1n \rightarrow {}^{139}Xe + {}^{95}Sr + 2\,{}^1n + Energy$$

The diagram, Fig. 4.7, below illustrates the above reaction.
  (i) Label all of the particles.
  (ii) Extend the diagram to illustrate how a chain reaction might develop.

Figure 4.7

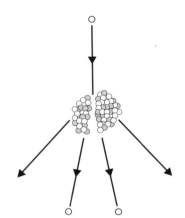

(2 marks)

  (iii) Why is proton bombardment unlikely to produce nuclear fission?

(2 marks)

  (iv) Use this data to show that the energy released in a single fission is about 3×10^{-11} J.

DATA

Particle	Mass/u
^{235}U	235.0
^{139}Xe	138.9
^{95}Sr	94.89
^1n	1.009

$1u = 1.7 \times 10^{-27}$ kg
$c\ \ = 3.0 \times 10^8$ m s^{-1}

(2 marks)

(b) Although the uranium fuel is enriched, only 3% of the uranium atoms in the fuel are the fissile ^{235}U isotope. The remaining 97% of the fuel is made up of ^{238}U.
  (i) Show that there are approximately 8×10^{23} atoms of ^{235}U in 10 kg of fuel. (The Avogadro constant $= 6.0 \times 10^{23}$ mol^{-1})
  (ii) How much energy is available if all of these atoms undergo fission?

(2 marks)

(c) The power needed for a submarine to travel at maximum speed is 750 kW. Show that 10 kg of fuel should last for at least one year.
    (1 year $= 3.2 \times 10^7$ s)

(2 marks)

(Oxford & Cambridge)

5 Electromagnetism

✓ **REVISION TIPS**

Formulae which you need to be familiar with or to learn. You must be sure which you need to know and which you will be given. Do you know what the symbols represent and can you name the units for each formula?

Field (or **flux density**) near current carrying wire $\quad B = \dfrac{\mu_0 I}{2\pi r}$

Field in centre of solenoid $\quad B = \dfrac{\mu_0 N I}{L}$

Force on a moving charge $\quad F = Bqv$

Force on wire carrying a current $\quad F = BIL$

Magnetic flux $\quad \phi = BA$

Flux linkage $\quad \Phi = N\phi$

Faraday's Law: Induced e.m.f. $\quad E = \dfrac{N\mathrm{d}\Phi}{\mathrm{d}t}$

Mutual induction $\quad E = \dfrac{-M\mathrm{d}I}{\mathrm{d}t}$

Self induction $\quad E = \dfrac{-L\mathrm{d}I}{\mathrm{d}t}$

Ratio of e.m.f.s in transformer $\quad \dfrac{E_s}{E_p} = \dfrac{N_s}{N_p}$

100% efficient transformer $\quad E_s I_s = E_p I_p$

Check that you know and understand the following ideas and terminology:

► Can you sketch the shape and direction of the field
   (a) around a straight wire carrying a current
   (b) inside a long solenoid?
► Can you apply Fleming's Left Hand Rule to the force on currents and moving charges?
► Can you distinguish between flux and flux density?
► Do you understand why a particle moving at right angles to a steady magnetic field describes circular motion? Can you derive the equation for the radius of this circle?
► Do you understand the circumstances in which an e.m.f. can be induced and what determines the magnitude and direction of the induced e.m.f.?
► Can you sketch and describe a typical transformer?
► Do you know the causes of inefficiency in a transformer?
► Why is electrical energy transmitted around the country at **high** voltages using **a.c.**?

TOPIC OUTLINE

Magnetic field (or flux density) B, unit T, tesla or Wbm^{-2}

Magnetic fields are created by permanent magnets or electromagnets and are regions where other magnets or electromagnets experience forces.

The strength of the field is determined from the force it exerts on a wire, length L, carrying a current I. It is the force per unit length per unit current.

$$B = \frac{F}{IL} \qquad \text{Units NA}^{-1}\,\text{m}^{-1} \text{ or T(tesla)}$$

The field created by current I flowing in a straight wire is set of concentric cylinders. You should remember the field direction and be able to use $B = \mu_0 I/2\pi r$ where r is the distance from wire. Note that the field is proportional to $1/r$, i.e. the field halves at twice the distance. For a **solenoid** the field is parallel to the axis, is uniform in the middle, and falls to half this value near the ends.

You should be able to use $B = \mu_0 NI/L$ for the uniform field in the middle section, i.e. field depends on current I and number of turns/m N/L.

Force on moving charges

A charge q moving at speed v, perpendicular to a magnetic field B, experiences a force $= Bqv$. The force is perpendicular to the field *and* to the direction of movement of charge. (Use Fleming's Left Hand Rule: **first** finger = **fi**eld, **se**cond finger = direction of positive **c**harge, thu**m**b = force (**m**otion.)

A constant force Bqv acting at right angles to direction of motion of charge q, makes it move round in a circle of radius r at constant speed v.

$$\text{Acceleration towards centre of circle} = \frac{v^2}{r}$$

So force $= \dfrac{mv^2}{r} = Bqv$. Rearranging gives $r = \dfrac{mv}{Bq}$.

Use this equation to determine how r depends on m, v, B, and q.

Forces on wires carrying currents

A wire of length L carrying current I perpendicular to a field B experiences force BIL. Use Fleming's Left Hand Rule for directions.

Definition of Ampere

Two wires 1 m apart each carrying a current of 1 Amp, each exert a force $= 2 \times 10^{-7}$ N on 1 m length of each other. If currents are in the *same* direction, the force is **attractive**.

It follows from this definition that μ_0 has the value $4\pi \times 10^{-7}$ Hm^{-1}.

Induced e.m.f.

An e.m.f. can be induced across a wire or coil by moving the wire through a magnetic field, rotating the coil in a magnetic field, jabbing a magnet in the coil or changing the magnetic field linked with the coil.

Flux $\phi = BA$, where A is the area 'cut' by the circuit, perpendicular to B. Units of ϕ are Wb (weber) i.e. flux = field (flux density) multiplied by the area.

Flux linkage $\Phi = N\phi$, i.e. flux multiplied by N, the number of turns.

Faraday's Law: Magnitude of induced e.m.f. = rate of change of flux linkage. i.e. induced e.m.f. $E = Nd\Phi/dt$

Lenz Law: direction of induced e.m.f. opposes change causing it.

An e.m.f. induced across a wire (or coil), will cause a current to flow if the wire forms part of a complete circuit.

Use Fleming's Right Hand Rule (**f**irst finger, **f**ield: thu**m**b, direction of **m**ovement of wire: se**c**ond finger, **c**urrent.

Mutual induction

A changing flux created by a changing current in one coil will induce an e.m.f. in a second coil linked with this *changing* flux.

E.m.f. induced in second coil, $E = -M \, dI/dt$ where M is mutual inductance, and dI/dt is the rate of change of current in the first coil.

Self induction

A changing flux created by an alternating current in a coil will induce an e.m.f. in that coil itself. From Lenz Law this induced e.m.f. must oppose the change, so is referred to as back e.m.f. The self induced e.m.f. $E = -L \, d/dt$ where L is self inductance of coil (in Henry).

Transformer

This consists of two coils wrapped on the same laminated iron core. An *alternating* e.m.f. E_p in the primary coil creates *changing* flux in the core, which *induces* an e.m.f. E_s in the secondary coil by mutual induction.

$E_s/E_p = N_s/N_p$, where N_s and N_p are the turns on the secondary and primary. If 100% efficient, then power out = power in,

i.e. $E_s I_s = E_p I_p$ where I_s and I_p are currents in coils.

In a step-up transformer: $E_s > E_p$ because $N_s > N_p$ and so $I_s < I_p$

Transmission of power at high voltages

A certain amount of power needs to be transmitted to the town. Power $= VI$, so if V is large, I will be *comparatively* small. As the current passes through the resistance R of the transmission lines electrical power $= I^2 R$ is converted to heat. Hence smaller I means less power wasted. Hence the voltage output at the power station is stepped up by a transformer so that the current I in the transmission lines is small. (*Tip.* If you apply $V = IR$ to the transmission line, you will simply calculate the voltage drop (p.d.) between the ends of the transmission line.)

r.m.s. voltage and current

If a power supply delivers a sinusoidally alternating voltage then the average voltage $= 0$. However the **average power** delivered to a lamp of resistance R is equal to the average (V^2/R). If V varies as a sine curve, then V^2 varies as $\sin^2$ and the average of $V^2 = (V_{max})^2/2$. Hence the **average power** $= (V_{max})^2/2R$. The **steady** voltage $V_{d.c.}$ which delivers the *same* power is known as the **root mean square (r.m.s.) voltage**, $V_{r.m.s.}$

Hence $\dfrac{(V_{d.c.})^2}{R} = \dfrac{(V_{max})^2}{2R}$, $(V_{d.c.})^2 = \dfrac{(V_{max})^2}{2}$ and $V_{d.c.} = \dfrac{V_{max}}{\sqrt{2}}$.

Hence $V_{r.m.s.} = \dfrac{V_{max}}{\sqrt{2}}$ and similarly $I_{r.m.s.} = \dfrac{I_{max}}{\sqrt{2}}$.

REVISION ACTIVITIES

You should have a copy of the formula sheet provided by your board on your desk. The following constants may be useful.

$\mu_0 = 4\pi \times 10^{-7} \, \text{Hm}^{-1}$ $e = 1.6 \times 10^{-19} \, \text{C}$ $m_e = 9.1 \times 10^{-31} \, \text{kg}$

1 Sketch the field associated with a straight wire carrying a current. Mark clearly the directions of the field and current.

2 Calculate:
(a) the field at a distance of 2 cm from a wire carrying a current of 5 A.
(b) What is the field strength at a distance of 2 mm?

3 Calculate the field at the centre of a solenoid of length 15 cm with 400 turns, which is carrying a current of 3 A.

4 Calculate:
(a) the force acting on an electron travelling at $3 \times 10^7 \, \text{m s}^{-1}$ at right angles to a magnetic field of flux density $4 \times 10^{-3} \, \text{T}$
(b) the resulting acceleration of the electron
(c) the radius of the circle the electron describes.

5 6 MW of power is transmitted at 200 000 V.
(a) What current will flow down the transmission cables?
(b) If the resistance of the cables is 5 Ω, how much power will be wasted (converted to heat) in the transmission lines?

6 If a sinusoidal voltage has an r.m.s. value of 5 V, what is the peak (maximum) voltage?

PRACTICE QUESTIONS

Question 1

(a) Figure 5.1 shows an arrangement for measuring the magnetic flux density B between the poles of a magnet.

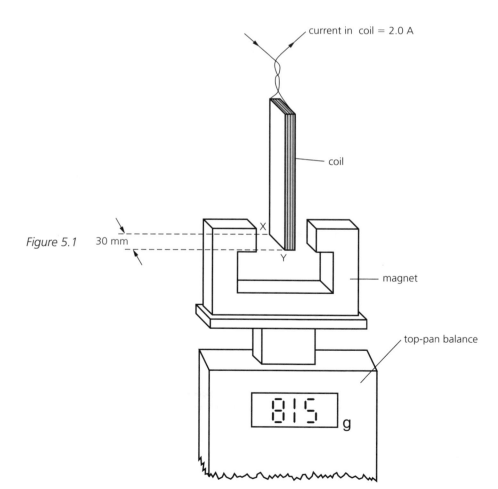

Figure 5.1

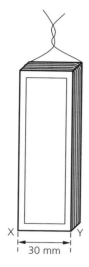

Figure 5.2

The coil shown in Figs 5.1 and 5.2 has 50 turns. Its lower side XY is horizontal and has a mean length of 30 mm.
Before the current is switched on, the balance reading is 850 gram. With a current of 2.0 A in the coil, the balance reading becomes 815 gram.

(i) The current in the lower side of the coil is in the direction X to Y in Fig. 5.1. What is the direction of the field of the magnet? Explain how you obtain your answer.

....

....

....

....

(ii) Calculate the magnetic flux density B between the poles of the magnet.

$B = $ .... *(6 marks)*

(b) Describe another way of determining B by a method which does not involve the measurement of masses or forces.

....

....

....

....

....

....

.... *(4 marks)*

(Cambridge)

Question 2

The equation $B = \dfrac{\mu_0 I}{2\pi a}$ gives the magnetic flux density due to a current flowing in a long straight wire at a point distance a from the centre of the wire.

(a) Draw a diagram showing a vertical wire carrying a current and three lines of the resulting magnetic field in a horizontal plane due to this current. Show the directions of the current and field on your diagram. *(3 marks)*

(b) A second vertical wire is arranged parallel to the first wire at a distance r from it as shown in the figure. A current I flows in each in the direction shown in Fig. 5.3.
Write down

(i) an equation for the magnetic flux density at Q due to the current in wire R,
(ii) an expression for the force on a length l of wire S due to this field,
(iii) the direction of this force,
(iv) the magnitude and direction of the force on a length l of wire R due to the field produced by wire S. *(4 marks)*

(c) Two long vertical wires, 15 mm apart, each carry a current of 5.0 A. The direction of the currents is as shown on the figure above.

(i) Calculate the force on a 3.0 m length of one of the wires.
(ii) What would be the effect on this force if the direction of **one** of the currents were to be reversed? *(2 marks)*

permeability of free space $\mu_0 = 4\pi \times 10^{-7}\,\text{Hm}^{-1}$ (NEAB)

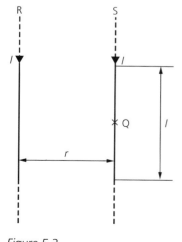

Figure 5.3

Question 3

(a) When positive ions of mass M and charge Q are accelerated across a potential difference V_0 they reach a speed v. Assuming that they have negligible kinetic energy before acceleration, use the principle of conservation of energy to show that

$$v = \sqrt{\frac{2QV_0}{M}}$$

. . . .

. . . .

. . . .

. . . . *(2 marks)*

(b) Fast-moving positive ions which have been accelerated as in (a) are then injected into a vacuum enclosure where a uniform electric field and a uniform magnetic field act simultaneously over the same path length.

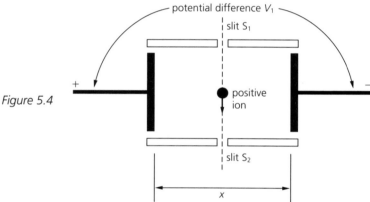

Figure 5.4

The electric field is created by a p.d. V_1 applied across two metal plates a distance x apart. The ions enter this region through slit S_1 and, if they are undeviated, leave through slit S_2, where S_1 and S_2 are aligned as shown in the diagram.

  (i) State the direction of the electric field.

. . . .

  (ii) State the direction in which the magnetic field should be applied if the ions are to emerge from S_2. Explain how you obtained your answer.

. . . .

. . . .

  (iii) Explain the force condition which must be satisfied if a beam of ions is to emerge from S_2.

. . . .

. . . .

(iv) Show that, if the ions emerge from S_2, the magnitude of the flux density of the magnetic field is given by

$$B = \frac{V_1}{x} \sqrt{\frac{M}{2QV_0}}$$

. . . .

. . . .

. . . .

. . . .

. . . . *(7 marks)*

(c) A narrow collimated beam of singly-charged positive ions, each of a mass 4.0×10^{-26} kg and travelling at 1.3×10^5 m s^{-1}, enters a uniform magnetic field which is directed at right angles to the beam. The ions are deflected into a semicircular path of diameter 0.60 m. Calculate the flux density of the magnetic field.
(charge of an electron $= -1.6 \times 10^{-19}$ C)

. . . .

. . . .

. . . .

. . . .

. . . . *(4 marks)*

(d) Using the same arrangement, some doubly-charged positive ions of the same element are injected into the same magnetic field at the same velocity as in (c). State and explain what effect this would have, compared with the singly-charged ions, on
  (i) the magnetic force experienced by an ion,

. . . .

. . . .

(ii) the diameter of the path of the ions.

. . . .

. . . . *(3 marks)*
(NEAB)

Question 4

Consider a long, air-cooled solenoid. For a given current in the solenoid, the magnetic flux density at a point on the axis near the middle of the solenoid depends on

1 the number of turns divided by the length of the solenoid.
2 the cross-sectional area of the solenoid.
3 the resistance of the solenoid.

Which of these statements is (are) correct?
A 1 only   **B** 2 only   **C** 3 only   **D** 1 and 2 only   **E** 1, 2 and 3
(NICCEA)

Question 5
A beam of charged particles is projected at right angles to a uniform magnetic field. The beam then follows a circular path.
Which of the following would increase the radius of the curvature of the path?

1 An increase in charge.
2 An increase in the mass of each particle.
3 A decrease in the flux density.

  A **1** and **2** only correct   **B** **2** and **3** only correct
  C **1** only correct   **D** **3** only correct   (AEB)

Question 6
(a) Figure 5.5 shows two coils X and Y wound on a soft-iron core.

Figure 5.5

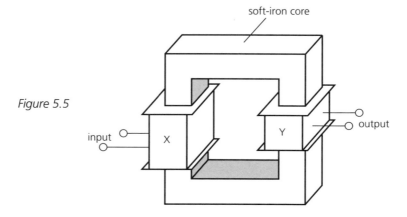

Magnetic flux links X and Y when there is a current in X.
 (i) Write down an equation for magnetic flux, explaining the symbols used. *(2 marks)*
 (ii) What happens in coil Y when the magnetic flux in the core changes? State a law that justifies your answer.

. . . .

. . . .

. . . .

. . . .

. . . .

. . . . *(2 marks)*

(b) (i) The input of coil X is now connected to a 240 V mains supply, the current from which changes direction 100 times per second. The output of coil Y is connected to a 12 V, 3 A light bulb. The bulb lights with full intensity. Use energy considerations to calculate the current in coil X. Assume that the efficiency of energy transfer between the two coils is 100%.

            current = ... *(2 marks)*

(ii) Suggest what would happen to the light bulb if a source supplying a constant 240 V were substituted for the mains supply. Give a reason for your answer.

. . . .

. . . .

. . . .

. . . . *(2 marks)*

(Cambridge)

Question 7

The magnetic flux density through a coil of N turns is increased uniformly from zero to a maximum value in time t. An e.m.f. V is induced.
The maximum flux through the coil is

A $\dfrac{VN}{t}$ **B** VNt **C** $\dfrac{V}{Nt}$ **D** $\dfrac{Vt}{N}$ (AEB)

Question 8

Two coils **A** and **B**, have inductances L_A and L_B and resistances R_A and R_B respectively. The graphs in Fig. 5.6 show the growth of current when each coil is connected in turn to the same cell.

Figure 5.6

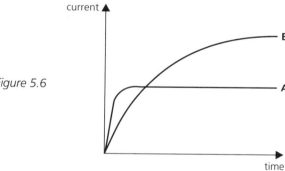

Which of the following statements is correct?
A $L_A < L_B$ and $R_A > R_B$ **B** $L_A < L_B$ and $R_A < R_B$
C $L_A > L_B$ and $R_A > R_B$ **D** $L_A > L_B$ and $R_A < R_B$ (AEB)

Question 9

Two coils placed close to one another have a mutual inductance of 20 mH. The current in one coil is reduced at a constant rate from 5.0 A in one direction to zero and is then increased, at the same rate, to 5.0 A in the opposite direction, all in a time of 2.0 s. What is the magnitude of the e.m.f. induced in the second coil?
A zero **B** 4.0 mV **C** 8.0 mV **D** 50 mV **E** 100 mV (NICCEA)

6 Gravitational and electrical field and potential

Formulae which you need to be familiar with or to learn. You must be sure which you need to know and which you will be given. Do you know what the symbols represent and can you name the units for each formula?

Gravitational fields

Force between two masses $F = \dfrac{Gm_1 m_2}{r^2}$

Field near planet $= \dfrac{GM_{\text{p}}}{R^2}$

Field at surface of Earth $g = \dfrac{GM_{\text{E}}}{R_{\text{E}}^2}$

Acceleration towards centre of circle $a = \dfrac{v^2}{R}$

Period of orbit $T = \dfrac{2\pi R_{\text{o}}}{v}$

Change in potential energy (p.e.) $= \dfrac{GMm}{R_1} - \dfrac{GMm}{R_2}$

Change in potential $\Delta V_{\text{G}} = \dfrac{GM}{R_1} - \dfrac{GM}{R_2}$

Absolute potential $V_{\text{G}} = \dfrac{-GM}{R}$

Electric fields

Force between two charges $F = \dfrac{Q_1 Q_2}{4\pi\varepsilon_{\text{o}} r^2}$

Field near charge $E = \dfrac{Q}{4\pi\varepsilon_{\text{o}} r^2}$

Change in potential energy (e.p.e.) $= \dfrac{Q_1 Q_2}{4\pi\varepsilon_{\text{o}} R_1} - \dfrac{Q_1 Q_2}{4\pi\varepsilon_{\text{o}} R_2}$

Change in potential $\Delta V_{\text{E}} = \dfrac{Q_1}{4\pi\varepsilon_{\text{o}} R_1} - \dfrac{Q_1}{4\pi\varepsilon_{\text{o}} R_2}$

Electric field $E = \dfrac{-\Delta V}{\Delta x}$ (potential gradient)

Check that you know and understand the following ideas and terminology:

▶ field strength (gravitational and electrical). Remember gravitational force = field × mass and electrical force = field × charge.

▶ that forces and fields surrounding point masses and charges obey inverse square laws.

▶ changes in gravitational and electrical energy and potential. Remember that the change in gravitational potential energy = change in potential × mass and change in electrical energy = change in potential × charge.

▶ absolute gravitational and electrical potential. Remember the convention that when masses or charges are a *long* way from each other, the potential energy and potential = 0. Hence if the force between two objects is *attractive*, then work has to be put *in* to *separate* the objects. The objects therefore have *more* energy when they are *separate* and so, by this convention, their energy when they are close is *negative*. The potential energy of two objects is *positive* if the force between them is one of *repulsion*. The same idea applies to potential.

▶ field lines and equipotentials and the relationship between them.

TOPIC OUTLINE

Gravitational field

This is a region where a **mass** experiences a **force**. Field strength is force on 1 kg, in $N\,kg^{-1}$.

The force in N acting on 1 kg of an object gives the acceleration of the object in ms^{-2}.

The **force of attraction** between two masses m_1 and m_2 is

$$F = \frac{Gm_1m_2}{r^2}$$

where r is the distance between the centres of mass of m_1 and m_2. G is the universal constant of Gravitation (units Nm^2kg^{-2})

This force obeys inverse square law, if r doubles the force quarters.

Field strength at distance R from the centre of a planet

(substituting $m_1 = M_p$, $m_2 = 1\,kg$) $= \dfrac{GM_p}{R^2}$

The Earth's field at the surface ($M_p = M_E$, $R = R_E$(Earth's radius)) $= \dfrac{GM_E}{R_E{}^2}$

The Earth's field also $= g = \dfrac{GM_E}{R_E{}^2} = 9.8\,Nkg^{-1}$ at surface.

Acceleration $g = 9.8\,m\,s^{-2}$.

A planet's **field** acting on moon or satellite (mass M_s) in orbit exerts a

force $= \dfrac{GM_pM_s}{R_o{}^2}$, where R_o is the distance between planet and satellite,

i.e. the radius of orbit.

Hence acceleration towards the centre of orbit $= \dfrac{v^2}{R_o} = \dfrac{GM_p}{R_o{}^2}$, where v is the speed of the satellite.

The time for one orbit (period) T = orbit length/speed. i.e. $T = \dfrac{2\pi R_o}{v}$.

Gravitational potential energy and potential
Increase in potential energy is the work done in moving a mass m away from another mass M.
Increase in **potential** is work done in moving **1 kg** away from another mass.

Change in potential energy $= \dfrac{GMm}{R_1} - \dfrac{GMm}{R_2}$ and change in

potential $= \dfrac{GM}{R_1} - \dfrac{GM}{R_2}$ where R_1 and R_2 are the starting and finishing

distances of m from M.
(Over small distances h where the force mg is assumed to be constant, the change in p.e. $= mgh$)

Absolute potential at distance R from mass $M = \dfrac{-GM}{R}$

i.e. potential at Earth's surface $= \dfrac{-GM_E}{R_E}$, and so $\dfrac{GM_E}{R_E}$ is the energy needed

to move 1 kg from the surface of the Earth to an infinite distance away.

Electric field

This is a region where a charge experiences a force. Field strength is the force on 1 C, in NC^{-1}.
Direction of field is direction of force on $+1$ C.

The force between two charges Q_1 and Q_2 is $F = \dfrac{Q_1 Q_2}{4\pi\varepsilon_0 r^2}$ where r is the

distance apart.
This is a force of **attraction** between **opposite** charges and **repulsion** between **like** charges.

The field at distance r from charge $Q (Q_2 = 1\text{ C}) = \dfrac{Q}{4\pi\varepsilon_0 r^2}$, which obeys the

inverse square law.

Electrical potential energy and potential
Increase in potential energy is the work done in moving charge Q_2 away from another charge Q_1 which is **attracting** it. It will be a **decrease** if the charges are **repelling**.

Change in potential energy $= \dfrac{Q_1 Q_2}{4\pi\varepsilon_0 R_1} - \dfrac{Q_1 Q_2}{4\pi\varepsilon_0 R_2}$ where R_1 and R_2 are the

final and initial distances of Q_2 from charge Q_1.

Change in potential is work done in moving **1 C** $= \dfrac{Q_1}{4\pi\varepsilon_0 R_1} - \dfrac{Q_1}{4\pi\varepsilon_0 R_2}$

$(Q_2 = 1\text{ C})$
The uniform (constant strength field) between two charged parallel plates is

a special case where the field $= \dfrac{V}{d}$, V is the p.d. between the plates and d is

the separation of the plates.

Field lines and equipotentials

Field lines are drawn to represent fields, with arrows showing the direction of the field. The field lines surrounding a point charge or mass are radial and the field lines between parallel plates are equally spaced. Lines of equipotential (equal potential) are perpendicular to field lines, because if a charge or mass is moved perpendicular to the field no work is done and so there is no change in potential energy. Lines of **equipotential** are usually drawn at **equal** intervals of **energy**. If the field is *uniform* the lines are *equally* *spaced* because in travelling the same distance the same work is done. Lines of equipotential become spaced *further apart* where the field is *weaker* because to do the *same* amount of work a *bigger* distance needs to be travelled.

Electric field $E = \dfrac{-\Delta V}{\Delta x}$ (potential gradient)

★ REVISION ACTIVITIES

You should have a copy of the formula sheet provided by your board on your desk.
The following constants may be useful.

$$G = 6.7 \times 10^{-11}\,\mathrm{Nm^2kg^{-2}} \qquad g = 9.8\,\mathrm{Nkg^{-1}} \qquad R_E = 6.4 \times 10^6\,\mathrm{m}$$
$$M_E = 6.0 \times 10^{24}\,\mathrm{kg} \qquad \varepsilon_0 = 8.8 \times 10^{-12}\,\mathrm{N^{-1}C^2m^{-2}}$$
$$e = 1.6 \times 10^{-19}\,\mathrm{C} \qquad m_e = 9.1 \times 10^{-31}\,\mathrm{kg}$$

1 Write down all the equations you need to *know* in this section, making sure you understand the symbols. In what situations can these be applied?

2 Calculate the force between two 5 kg masses placed 10 cm apart.

3 Calculate the force between two charges of 6 nC placed 2 cm apart.

4 (a) Calculate the field between two parallel plates 5 cm apart, with a p.d. of 3000 V across them.
   (b) What will the force on 1 electron placed between these plates?

5 Calculate g from G, R_E and M_E only.

6 (a) What is the period of a geo-stationary satellite?
   (b) Calculate the radius of orbit of a geo-stationary satellite.
   (c) What is (i) the speed, and (ii) the k.e. if the mass of the satellite = 3000 kg?
   (d) How much energy is required to lift the satellite from the surface of the Earth to the height of its orbit.

7 Derive an expression for and calculate the 'escape velocity' of an object from the surface of the Earth.

8 Sketch the fields
   (a) surrounding a point positive charge
   (b) between a pair of charged parallel plates.
   Make sure you have indicated the direction of the fields. Add to your diagrams lines representing equipotentials. How did you decide on the spacing of the equipotentials?

H I N T 6(b)

Equate the force acting on it to the mass × acceleration towards the centre of the circle. Then combine this equation with the equation relating the period, speed and radius.

H I N T 6(d)

Calculate the change in p.e. of the 3000 kg mass.

H I N T 7

Equate kinetic energy to the energy needed to move mass to infinity.

？ PRACTICE QUESTIONS

Question 1

Figure 6.1 illustrates a model of a hydrogen atom. The model resembles that of a Sun-planet system (Fig. 6.2).

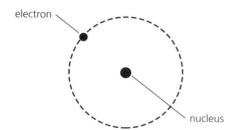

Figure 6.1

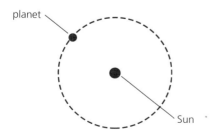

Figure 6.2

The electron follows a circular orbit around the nucleus. The planet follows a circular orbit around the Sun.

(a) Write down equations, identifying all symbols used, for
- (i) the electrical force F_E which holds the electron in orbit, (2 marks)
- (ii) the gravitational force F_G which holds the planet in orbit. (2 marks)

(b) By giving appropriate definitions, explain whether
- (i) the electric potential in the field of the nucleus,
- (ii) the gravitational potential in the field of the Sun

has a positive or a negative value.

electrical potential . . . .

. . . .

. . . .

gravitational potential . . . .

. . . .

. . . . (4 marks)

(Cambridge)

Question 2

The gravitational field strength at the surface of a star of radius 1.0×10^{10} m and mass 5.6×10^{33} kg is 4.0×10^3 N kg^{-1}.

(a) (i) Sketch a graph showing the variation of the magnitude of gravitational field strength with distance d from the centre of the star, for values of d which are greater than the radius of the star.

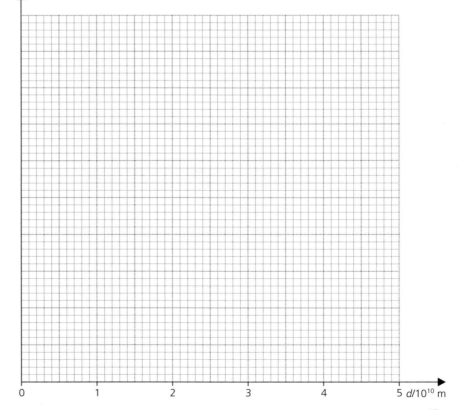

Figure 6.3

(2 marks)

(ii) Calculate the gravitational field strength of the star at a distance of 4.0×10^{17} m from its centre.

The universal gravitational constant, $G = 6.7 \times 10^{-11} \, \text{Nm}^2 \, \text{kg}^{-2}$.

(b) A second star, of mass 2.0×10^{30} kg is 4.0×10^{17} m from the first star. Calculate the force acting on the second star due to the gravitational field of the first.

(2 marks)

(AEB)

Question 3

Figure 6.4

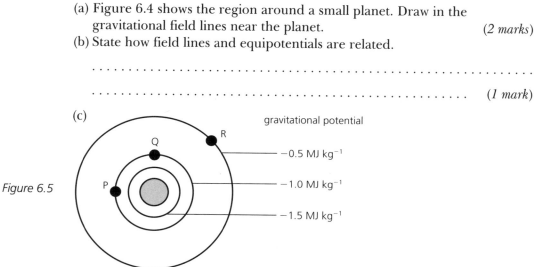

(a) Figure 6.4 shows the region around a small planet. Draw in the gravitational field lines near the planet.   *(2 marks)*

(b) State how field lines and equipotentials are related.

. . . .

. . . .   *(1 mark)*

(c)

Figure 6.5

Figure 6.5 shows a series of equipotentials around the planet. Values of the gravitational potential are given on the diagram. A spacecraft of mass 3000 kg orbits the planet. Calculate, showing your reasoning, the changes in the gravitational potential energy of the spacecraft when it moves from

(i) P to Q

. . . .

. . . .   *(2 marks)*

(ii) Q to R

. . . .

. . . .

. . . .   *(2 marks)*

(d) With reference to Fig. 6.5 explain why
 (i) the potentials all have a negative sign,

. . . .

. . . . *(1 mark)*

 (ii) the equipotential surfaces are spheres centred on the centre of the planet.

. . . .

. . . . *(1 mark)*

 (iii) equal changes in potential do not occur for equal changes in radius.

. . . .

. . . .

. . . . *(2 marks)*

(Cambridge)

Question 4

Each diagram shows a charged particle moving in an electric field. The direction of motion of the particle is shown by an arrow and, for each situation, the charged particle is labelled and also named underneath each diagram. For each case
 (i) show, on the diagram, the direction of the electric force,
 (ii) calculate the magnitude of the electric force on the particle.

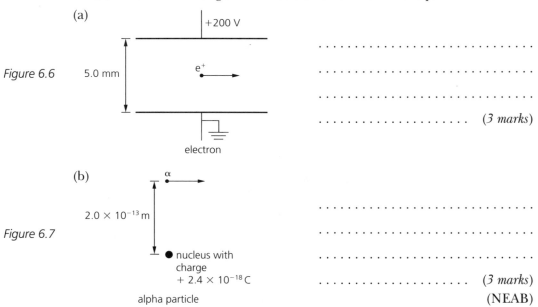

(a)

Figure 6.6

. . . .

. . . .

. . . .

. . . . *(3 marks)*

(b)

Figure 6.7

. . . .

. . . .

. . . .

. . . . *(3 marks)*

(NEAB)

Question 5

The rings of the planet Saturn consist of a vast number of small particles, each in a circular orbit about the planet. Two of the rings are shown in the diagram, Fig. 6.8.

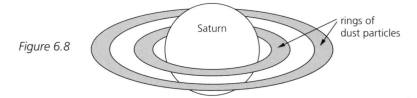

Figure 6.8

The inner edge of the inner ring is 70 000 km from the centre of the planet and the outermost edge of the outer ring is 140 000 km from the centre. The speed of the outermost particles is $17 \, \text{km s}^{-1}$.

(a) Show that the speed, v, of a particle in an orbit of radius r around a planet of mass M is given by

$$v = \sqrt{\frac{GM}{r}}$$

where G is the universal gravitational constant, $6.7 \times 10^{-11} \, \text{N m}^2 \, \text{kg}^{-2}$.

(b) Determine the mass of Saturn.

(c) How long does it take for the outermost particles to complete an orbit?

(d) Calculate the orbital speed of the particles nearest to Saturn.   (*7 marks*)

(AEB)

Question 6

The diagram in Fig. 6.9 shows a uniform electric field in which the lines of equal potential are spaced 5.0 cm apart.

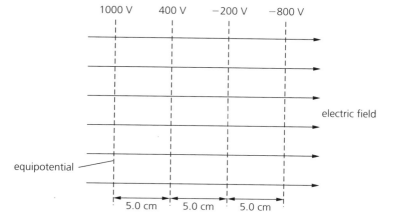

Figure 6.9

What is the value of the electric force which is exerted on a charge of $+2.0 \, \mu\text{C}$ when placed in the field?

A $1.2 \times 10^{-2} \, \text{N}$ **B** $2.4 \times 10^{-2} \, \text{N}$ **C** $2.4 \times 10^{4} \, \text{N}$
D $1.2 \times 10^{4} \, \text{N}$ **E** $2.4 \times 10^{-4} \, \text{N}$

Question 7

Figure 6.10 shows two points P and Q in a certain electric field. The distance PQ is L. R is a point on the line joining PQ, a distance x from P. The graph shows how the electric potential V at the point R depends on x.

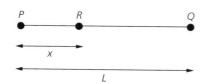

Figure 6.10

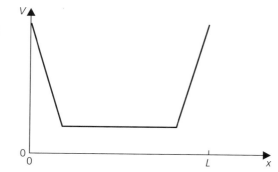

Which graph in Fig. 6.11 shows the variation with x of the electric field strength E, directed along the line PQ?

Figure 6.11

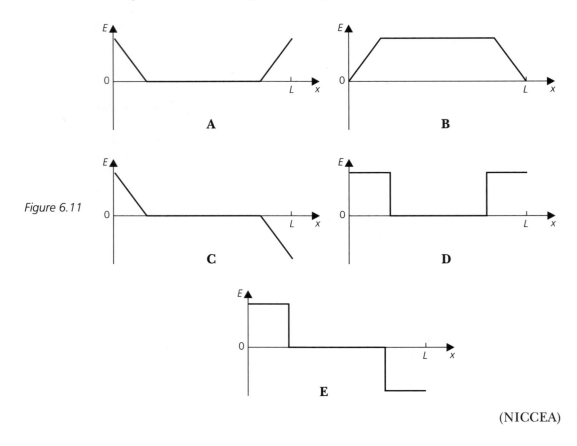

(NICCEA)

7 Thermal physics and matter

Formulae which you need to be familiar with or to learn. You must be sure which you need to know and which you will be given. Do you know what the symbols represent and can you state the units for each formula?

Hooke's Law	$F = -kx$
Young modulus	$E = \dfrac{\text{stress}}{\text{strain}}$
	$= \dfrac{(F/A)}{(e/l)}$
Energy stored	$\frac{1}{2}\dfrac{EAe^2}{l}$
Energy per unit volume	$\frac{1}{2}$ stress $\times$ strain
Pressure in kinetic theory	$p = \frac{1}{3}Nm <c^2>$
Mean square speed	$<c^2> = \dfrac{(c_1{}^2 + c_2{}^2 + c_3{}^3 + \ldots c_N{}^2)}{N}$
Average energy of a monatomic molecule	$\frac{3}{2}kT$
Celsius scale	$\dfrac{\theta\,^{\circ}\mathrm{C}}{100} = \dfrac{X_\theta - X_o}{X_{100} - X_o}$
Absolute scale	$T = 273.16\, p_T/p_{tr}$
Thermal conductivity	$\dfrac{dQ}{dt} = kA\dfrac{(\theta_2 - \theta_1)}{l}$
First law of thermodynamics	$\Delta Q = \Delta U + \Delta W = \Delta U + p\Delta V$

Vocabulary to check

Check that you know the following terms:

Matter: stress, strain, Young modulus, strong, stiff, ductile, brittle, malleable, plastic, elastic, hysteresis, Hooke's Law, ionic, covalent, diffusion, Brownian motion.

In **thermal physics** check that you are clear about the following definitions:

Thermal or heat capacity (C): the quantity of heat required to raise the temperature of a body by 1 degree.
Specific heat capacity (c): the heat capacity per unit mass, i.e. per kg.
Molar heat capacity of a gas at constant volume (C_v): the quantity of thermal energy required to produce a 1 degree rise in temperature of a gas when the volume is kept constant.

Molar heat capacity of a gas at constant pressure (C_p): the quantity of thermal energy required to produce a 1 degree rise in temperature of a gas when the pressure is kept constant.

Specific latent heat of fusion (l_f): the quantity of thermal energy required to change unit mass of a substance from solid to liquid without change of temperature.

Specific latent heat of vaporisation (l_v): the quantity of thermal energy required to change unit mass of a substance from liquid to vapour without change of temperature.

(Note for these last two the terms enthalpy change and specific enthalpy change are sometimes used. An *enthalpy* change is a change which takes place at constant pressure.)

In thermal physics you need to take care in the use of certain terminology when reading questions, and when writing answers:

▶ Strictly speaking the term *gas* should only be used when above the substance's *critical temperature*. This is the temperature above which the gas cannot be liquified by compression alone. The term *vapour* is used below this temperature. Below the critical temperature liquefaction can occur by simply compressing the gas. When a closed vessel contains a vapour in equilibrium with its liquid the vapour is called a *saturated vapour*, otherwise it is *unsaturated*.

▶ The term 'heat' is frequently misused. Students sometimes think of a hot body having 'heat inside it'. You should say that a hot body has internal energy and its internal energy increases when it is supplied with heat. Some authors suggest you should use heat only as a verb as in 'the water was heated.'

Useful tips in indicator diagram calculations

▶ Remember that the internal energy U of an ideal gas depends only on the temperature of the gas.

▶ Be careful with the sign convention used for the first law. In Longman texts we use the convention: ΔQ is positive if heat is supplied to the gas and negative if heat is transferred from it, and ΔW is positive if the gas expands to do external work and negative if it is compressed, i.e. if work is done on it. In an adiabatic change no heat enters or leaves the system, i.e. $\Delta Q = 0$, and so $-\Delta U = \Delta W$ so any external work is performed at the expense of the internal energy. But note that some boards employ a variation on this sign convention.

TOPIC OUTLINE

The terms stress and strain are used in the study of solids under forces of tension and compression. **Stress**, F/A, where F is the force acting on unit cross-sectional area A, can be either **tensile**, as when the solid is stretched, or **compressive**, if it is compressed. **Strain**, e/l where e is the extension and l the original length, is the fractional change in length.

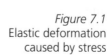

Figure 7.1
Elastic deformation
caused by stress

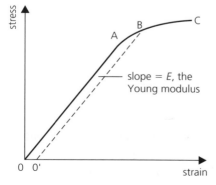

A stress–strain graph is used to describe the behaviour of a material with the advantage that it is characteristic of the material so that direct comparisons between the stress–strain graphs for different materials can be made when the dimensions of the specimens are different, e.g. a steel rod can be compared with a copper wire.

The gradient of the graph is E, the **Young modulus**. $E = Fl/Ae$. Point B identifies the **Yield Point** beyond which the sample starts to behave **plastically**. At C the sample breaks: the **Breaking Stress** is the greatest stress a material can withstand without fracture. The energy per unit volume stored in a stretched wire is given by $\frac{1}{2}$ stress $\times$ strain.

Crystalline solids occur when the atoms, ions or molecules are found in a regular repeating structure called a **lattice**. Most metals are actually crystalline, but with the crystal structure only apparent at a microscopic level. **Amorphous** or **glassy** materials do not have the same degree of order. **Polymeric** materials are made of long chains consisting of hundreds or thousands of identical units, each unit itself a small molecule.

The gaseous state of matter is the state in which the molecules are no longer in close contact with each other but move separately throughout the space available to them. The gas laws, Boyle's, Charles', and the pressure law provide a good description of both gases and unsaturated vapours. The three are combined in the **general gas equation**.

$$pV = nRT$$

where p is in Pa, V in m^3, n is the number of moles of gas present, and R is the molar gas constant. This equation is also the basis of the **absolute temperature scale**. Temperature scales such as the **Celsius scale** based upon the properties of a particular substance such as the expansion of mercury, depend upon the ability to reproduce two temperatures, in this case the freezing and boiling points of water 0 °C and 100 °C. A temperature θ is then defined as

$$\frac{\theta \,°C}{100} = \frac{X_\theta - X_0}{X_{100} - X_0}$$

where X_θ, X_0, and X_{100} are the material measurements at the three temperatures. On the absolute scale the two temperatures are the absolute zero defined as 0K and the triple point of water defined as 273.16 K and the pressure of the gas at constant volume is usually measured. A temperature is then defined as

$$T = 273.16 \frac{p_T}{p_{tr}}$$

where p_T is the pressure at the temperature and p_{tr} the pressure at the triple point.

The **kinetic theory model** of a gas is one in which the gas molecules are in constant motion, colliding elastically with each other and with their enclosing container. These bombardments give rise to the observed pressure. The theory leads to the formula, $p = \frac{1}{3} Nm <c^2>$ where N is the number of molecules per unit volume, m the molecular mass, and $<c^2>$ the mean square speed of the molecules. Comparison with the general gas equation shows that the temperature is proportional to the mean molecular kinetic energy. For a monotomic gas this is described by the formula, $\frac{1}{2}m <c^2> = \frac{3}{2} kT$ where k is the **Boltzmann constant** defined as the gas constant R divided by the Avogadro constant, the number of particles in a mole.

Experimental evidence in support of the kinetic theory of gases is provided by the phenomena of **diffusion** and **Brownian motion**.

Thermal energy, sometimes called **internal energy** U, is transferred within and between substances by conduction, convection and radiation. All bodies absorb and emit electromagnetic **radiation**. For example the earth absorbs radiation from the sun. It also emits radiation into space and remains in equilibrium at a temperature where the rate at which it gains energy is equal to the rate at which it loses it.

Natural convection currents exist in liquids and gases and are caused by movements due to density changes when there is heating or cooling. **Forced convection** is the process of forcing a liquid or gas past a hot body, such as an electrical heating element, in order to assist in the transfer of energy.

Conduction, a slow process in insulators, but a rapid process in metals, is important in solids. The process is described by the **thermal conductivity equation**,

$$\frac{dQ}{dt} = -kA\frac{(\theta_2 - \theta_1)}{l}$$

where dQ/dt is the rate of flow of heat, θ_1 and θ_2 are the temperatures at either end of the sample, l is its thickness, and k is the coefficient of thermal conductivity. In problems of heat transfer the concepts of **heat capacity** and **specific latent heat** are also important, as well as specific and molar heat capacity (see Revision Tips).

Thermodynamics is the branch of physics concerned with processes in which heat flows in or out of a 'system', whilst work is done on or by the 'system'. A simple example is the gas in the cylinder of a petrol engine. In thermodynamics 'heat' is energy which is transferred by conduction, convection, or radiation from one body to another, because one body is at a higher temperature than the other, and 'work' is transferred from one system to another by a force moving through a distance.

The **first law of thermodynamics** is really a statement of the principle of the conservation of energy and states that when an amount of heat ΔQ is applied to, say a gas (but equally to any system) the effect is to increase the internal energy of the gas by an amount ΔU and generate external work of an amount ΔW so that $\Delta Q = \Delta U + \Delta W$

For gas engines, the changes are usually shown on a p,V graph called an **indicator diagram**. **Adiabatic** changes are those where ΔQ is zero and there is no transfer of heat. **Isothermal changes** are those which occur without temperature change. The work done ΔW is equal to $p\Delta V$. The changes of the pressure and volume of the gas are then described by the general gas equation in its form for a fixed mass of gas:

$$\frac{p_1 V_1}{T_1} = \frac{p_2 V_2}{T_2}$$

REVISION ACTIVITIES

Check that you can do the following:

1   Define the following in words using formulae where appropriate: elastic limit, yield point, breaking stress, polymer, absolute temperature scale, degree Celsius, degree kelvin, specific heat of fusion, first law of thermodynamics.
2   Draw a force extension graph to describe the loading of a copper wire. Use the graph to identify the work done in loading the wire. Derive the formula $\frac{1}{2}$ stress × strain for the energy stored per unit volume in a loaded wire.

3   Write down all the assumptions made in a simple version of the kinetic theory of gases. Use the theory to show that the temperature is proportional to the mean kinetic energy of a gas molecule.

4   Look up in a textbook the methods for determining the coefficients of thermal conductivity of a good conductor and a poor conductor. Write out three differences in the methods and reasons for these differences.

5   Calculate the flow rate of water through a shower which is heated by a 7 kW electric element, the water being warmed from 15 °C to 45 °C.

PRACTICE QUESTIONS

Question 1

The table gives corresponding values of load and extension when masses are hung on a wire of length 1.5 m and diameter 0.30 mm.

load/N	0.0	2.0	4.0	6.0	8.0	10.0	11.0	11.2
extension/mm	0.0	1.0	2.1	3.1	4.2	5.4	7.3	9.0

(a) (i) Plot a graph of load (vertical axis) against extension (horizontal axis).
    (ii) Indicate on your graph the region over which Hooke's Law is obeyed.
                                                                        (5 marks)
(b) Use your graph to calculate a value for the Young Modulus of the material from which the wire is made.

. . . .

. . . .

. . . . (4 marks)
                                                                                    (NEAB)

Question 2

At pressure P and absolute temperature T a mass M of an ideal gas fills a closed container of volume V. An *additional* mass $2M$ of the same gas is introduced into the container and the volume is then reduced to $\frac{V}{3}$ and the temperature to $\frac{T}{3}$. Which one of the following gives the new pressure of the gas?

A $\frac{P}{3}$ B P C $3P$ D $9P$
                                                        (AEB – specimen question)

Question 3

(a) Explain what is meant by the *root mean square speed* of the molecules in a gas.   (2 marks)
(b) Four molecules, each of mass 5.2×10^{-26} kg, move in a horizontal plane with velocities 800 m s^{-1} northwards, 200 m s^{-1} eastwards, 400 m s^{-1} southwards and 500 m s^{-1} westwards, respectively. Calculate, for these four molecules,
   (i) the mean momentum,
   (ii) the mean kinetic energy.   (7 marks)
                                                                                    (NEAB)

Question 4

A student pours 500 g of water into an aluminium saucepan of mass 1.20 kg, heats it over a steady flame and records the temperature as it heats up. The temperatures are plotted as shown overleaf.

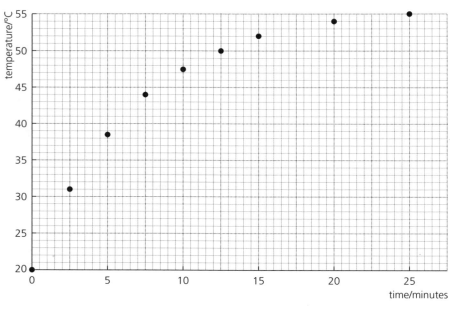

Figure 7.2

Calculate the total heat capacity of the saucepan and water.

Specific heat capacity of water   = 4200 J kg^{-1} K^{-1}.
Specific heat capacity of aluminium =   900 J kg^{-1} K^{-1}.

. . . .

. . . .

. . . .

Heat capacity = ...   (3 marks)

Find the rate of rise of water temperature at the beginning of the heating process.

. . . .

. . . .

Rate of rise of temperature = ...   (2 marks)

Find the rate at which energy is supplied to the saucepan and water.

. . . .

. . . .

Rate of energy supply = ...   (2 marks)

Explain why the rate at which the temperature rises slows down progressively as the heating process continues.

. . . .

. . . .

. . . .

. . . .   (2 marks)
(London)

Question 5

(a) State the relationship between the energy of the molecules of a perfect gas and
    (i) the temperature of the gas.
    (ii) the internal energy of the gas.   (2 marks)

(b) A sample of hot liquid is allowed to cool naturally in a test tube. The temperature of the liquid is recorded at various times as the liquid cools and the results are shown in Fig. 7.3.

Figure 7.3

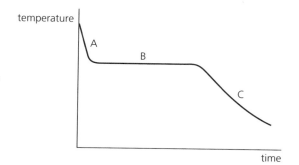

(i) Describe and explain what is happening in the test tube during each of the time intervals corresponding to the regions labelled A, B and C.
(ii) By reference to A, B and C explain the shape of each portion of the graph.
(iii) State whether the material in the test tube has a higher specific heat capacity in region A or in region C. Explain your answer. (*10 marks*)

(NEAB)

Question 6

The gas in an engine, which is considered to be an ideal gas, undergoes a cycle of changes of volume V, pressure p and temperature T, as illustrated in Fig. 7.4.

Figure 7.4

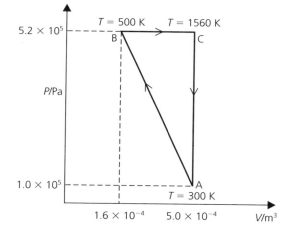

(a) By using the equation of state for an ideal gas show that the amount of gas is 0.020 mol. (*3 marks*)
(b) Complete the following table. Start by finding the work done on the gas during each of the three stages and then use the first law of thermodynamics to determine those values which are not given. (*7 marks*)

Stage	Increase in internal energy/J	Work done on gas/J	Heat supplied to gas/J
A → B			−22
B → C			+618
C → A			

(Cambridge)

Question 7

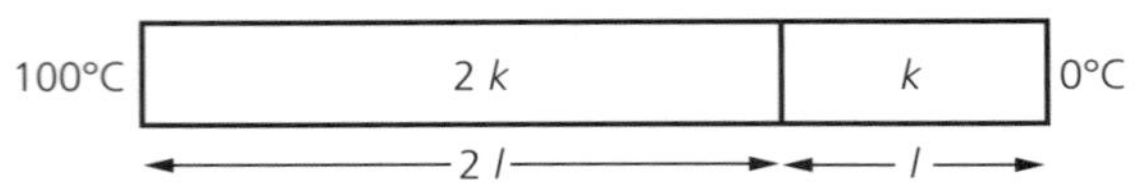

Figure 7.5

A lagged rod of length $2l$, and made of metal of thermal conductivity $2k$ is in thermal contact with a lagged rod of equal cross section and of length l and thermal conductivity k. A temperature difference of 100 °C is maintained across the combination as shown. What is the temperature of the junction, in °C?

A 25   **B** 33.3   **C** 50   **D** 66.7   (AEB)

Question 8

(a) Define the *thermal conductivity* of a material.   *(3 marks)*
(b) A layer of ice 20 mm thick has formed on the surface of a pond on a day when the temperature of the air in contact with the ice is −4.0 °C. If the temperature of the water beneath the ice is 0 °C, calculate
   (i) the temperature gradient at a point in the ice,
   (ii) the rate of flow of heat by conduction through each square metre of the ice.   *(4 marks)*
(c) The thickness of the ice is later found to have increased by 1.0 mm.
   (i) Calculate the mass of the additional ice which has formed under each square metre of the surface.
   (ii) Determine the energy which must have been removed from the water to form each square metre of the new ice layer.
   (iii) Hence estimate the time taken for the additional ice to form.   *(4 marks)*

specific latent heat of fusion of ice $= 3.3 \times 10^5 \, \mathrm{J \, kg^{-1}}$
thermal conductivity of ice $= 2.1 \, \mathrm{W \, m^{-1} \, K^{-1}}$
density of ice $= 910 \, \mathrm{kg \, m^{-3}}$ (NEAB)

Question 9

The e.m.f. of a certain thermocouple with one junction X in melting pure ice and the other Y in steam from water boiling at standard pressure is 4.1 mV. With X still in the melting ice, and Y in a certain boiling liquid, the e.m.f. is 11.6 mV. Deduce the boiling point of the liquid on the centigrade scale of the thermoelectric thermometer.   *(3 marks)*

Question 10

Explain the meanings of the terms *specific heat capacity* and *specific latent heat of vaporisation*.   *(4 marks)*
Figure 7.6 shows a continuous flow apparatus for determining the specific latent heat of vaporisation of a liquid. The experiment is performed twice with different values of voltage and current. On each occasion a constant rate of flow of condensed liquid is achieved.

	Voltage (V)	Current (A)	Flow rate/kg s⁻¹
Experiment 1	16.0	5.0	3.5×10^{-5}
Experiment 2	24.0	7.5	8.0×10^{-5}

   (i) Explain why it is important to achieve a constant flow rate and suggest how it could be confirmed in the experiment that this condition is met.   *(2 marks)*
   (ii) Use the above data to determine a value for the specific latent heat of vaporisation of the liquid.   *(6 marks)*

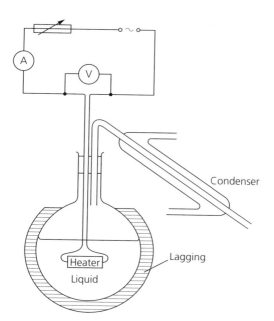

Figure 7.6

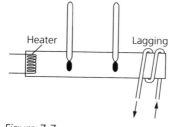

Figure 7.7

Question 11

(a) Describe how heat is transferred from a hotter region of a gas to a cooler region by conduction, convection, and radiation. *(4 marks)*

(b) Figure 7.7 shows part of an apparatus for determining the thermal conductivity k of a good conductor.

   (i) State the measurements that must be made in this determination, and explain how these measurements are combined to give a value for k. *(5 marks)*

   (ii) Outline the experimental precautions observed during this determination. *(2 marks)*

   (iii) What would be the effects on the readings and the results of this determination if the lagging were removed? *(2 marks)*

(c) An electronic device operates at 80 °C and generates heat at a power of 3.0 W. It is attached (see below) to an aluminium rod of length 20 mm and area of cross-section 50 mm².

The device and the rod are thermally insulated and heat is removed at the other end of the rod by a finned heat-sink. The heat-sink can transfer heat to its surroundings at a power of 90 W per square metre of its surface per kelvin of excess temperature over its surroundings.

(Take the thermal conductivity of aluminium to be $200 \, \mathrm{W \, m^{-1} \, K^{-1}}$.)

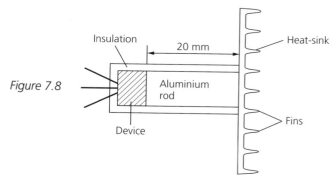

Figure 7.8

   (i) If the surroundings are at 20 °C, what area of heat sink is required and what is its equilibrium temperature? *(5 marks)*

   (ii) Discuss whether the equilibrium temperature will be different if the device does not make good contact with the rod. *(2 marks)*

(Oxford)

Question 12

In the hair drier shown in the diagram air is drawn through the system by a fan. The air is warmed as it passes the heating elements.

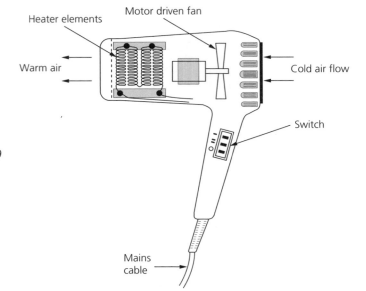

Figure 7.9

The hair drier has the option of using one heating element on its own or two heating elements in parallel. Each element provides 600 W when operated at 240 V.

There are also two fan speeds, the volume flow rate automatically increasing when both heating elements are used.

The effective specific heat capacity of the air is $990\,\mathrm{J\,kg^{-1}\,K^{-1}}$.

The density of air is $1.25\,\mathrm{kg\,m^{-3}}$ at $60\,°\mathrm{C}$.

(a) In one case the ambient temperature is $20\,°\mathrm{C}$. When one 600 W element is used and the fan is run at its slower speed, the temperature of the air leaving the drier is $60\,°\mathrm{C}$.

    Calculate:
    (i) the mass flow rate;
    (ii) the volume flow rate.   *(5 marks)*

(b) When the second element is switched on the temperature of the air from the drier rises to $75\,°\mathrm{C}$.

    Calculate the new mass flow rate of the air.   *(3 marks)*

(c) Explain why it would be unwise to design the drier so that both heating elements are used without an increase in the volume flow rate.   *(2 marks)*

(d) Determine the supply current when both heating elements are on, neglecting the current in the fan.   *(2 marks)*

(e) The heating element is cooled by the process of *forced convection*.

    (i) How does *forced convection* differ from *natural convection*?
    (ii) The equation which relates to cooling by forced convection is

$$\frac{\mathrm{d}\theta}{\mathrm{d}t} = -k(\theta - \theta_0)$$

        State in your own words what this equation expresses in mathematical terms.

    (iii) Use the equation to explain what happens to the hot air temperature when the hair drier is used in colder conditions.   *(6 marks)*

(f) State and explain what would happen if the fan were to stop working.

                                                          (2 marks)

                                                                (AEB)

Solutions
Forces in static and dynamic situations

SOLUTIONS TO REVISION ACTIVITIES

1 Vectors are force, velocity, acceleration, momentum. The rest are scalars.
2 N, W, $\mathrm{m\,s^{-1}}$, $\mathrm{m\,s^{-2}}$, $\mathrm{m\,s^{-1}}$, $\mathrm{kg\,m\,s^{-1}}$, J, J.
3 $3.3\,\mathrm{m\,s^{-1}}$, $4.5 \times 10^4\,\mathrm{m\,s^{-1}}$, $1.40\,\mathrm{W}$.
6 Centripetal force is the inward force which produces, through Newton's second law, motion in a circle. Centrifugal force is the apparent outward force experienced by a body in circular motion when observed from its own circularly moving vantage point.

ANSWERS TO PRACTICE QUESTIONS

Question 1

(i) Note that both the force F and the 60 N force act through O and so their resultant force must also act through O. When the wheel is just starting to pivot about X it is not resting on the ground. Consequently the only other force acting on it is at X, and because it is not moving the nett forces acting must be zero. Hence this force must be equal and opposite to the resultant of F and the 60 N. In directional terms this force must also act through O. *(1 mark)*

(ii) To calculate the moment of the weight about X see the diagram below.

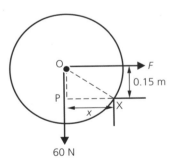

Applying Pythagoras' theorem to the triangle OXP we get

HINT
Mathematicians will note the 3, 4, 5 triangle

$(0.25)^2 = (0.15)^2 + x^2$ *(1 mark)*

Hence $x = 0.2\,\mathrm{m}$. *(1 mark)*

HINT
Don't forget the units and the sense of rotation for full marks

Hence the moment is $60\,\mathrm{N} \times 0.2\,\mathrm{m}$
$= 12\,\mathrm{Nm}$ in an anticlockwise sense. *(2 marks)*

HINT
Take moments about X so that the moment of the force through X is zero

(iii) Taking moments about X, $F \times 0.15 = 12\,\mathrm{Nm}$. *(2 marks)*

Hence $F = 80\,\mathrm{N}$ *(2 marks)*

Question 2

(a) The sum of the clockwise moments caused by external forces about any point is equal to the sum of the anticlockwise moments about that point. In addition the sum of the components of each of the forces in any direction is zero.
(2 marks)

(b) (i) The cable tension = weight of girder

$$= 500 \times 10 = 5000 \, \text{N}$$
(1 mark)

(ii)   ***Examiner's note*** To compute the tension, *T*, in PQR at least two methods can be applied.

(I) You can apply the triangle of forces (see Longman Study Guide page 16) by recognising that the three forces acting at Q are in equilibrium.

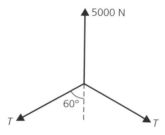

Thus they form a triangle of forces, viz

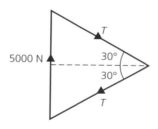

(1 mark)

Geometry on either half of the triangle gives

$$\frac{2500}{T} = \sin 30°$$

giving $\dfrac{2500}{T} = \dfrac{1}{2}$ Hence $T = 5000 \, \text{N}$ *(1 mark)*

or (II) You can simply recognise that the components of the two tensions *T downwards* must equal 5000 N.   *(1 mark)*

$$2T \cos 60° = 5000 \, \text{N}$$

giving $T = 5000 \, \text{N}$ *(1 mark)*

(iii) Let the required tension be *x*. If the crane is about to topple over the sum of the clockwise moments about the front foot must be equal to the sum of the anticlockwise moments.   *(1 mark)*

The external forces which act are as shown; these are the weight of the jib and cab and the upward reaction force of the ground which acts, when just about to topple, on the front leg only.

Thus the upward force is the weight of the girders (x) plus the weight of the jib and the crane

i.e. $x + 20\,000 \times 10 + 2500 \times 10$

Applying the principle of moments:

$200\,000 \times 2 = 25\,000 \times 4.5 + x \times 9$

giving $x = 31\,944.4\,\text{N}$ *(1 mark)*

(iv) This is equivalent to a load of $3194.4\,\text{kg}$.
If each girder has a mass of $500\,\text{kg}$ the maximum number of girders which can be lifted before the condition of toppling is reached is
$\dfrac{3000}{500} = 6$ *(1 mark)*

Question 3

(a) Acceleration is the rate of change of velocity with time, having regard to both magnitude and direction.   *(1 mark)*

(b) (i) Assuming $g = 9.81\,\text{m s}^{-2}$
To calculate t the time to reach the water use $s = ut + \frac{1}{2}at^2$

Thus we have $u = 0$ (no initial velocity)
and $s = 36\,\text{m}$
so $36 = \frac{1}{2} \times 9.81 \times t^2$ *(1 mark)*
giving $t = \sqrt{7.34}$
$ = 2.71\,\text{s}$ *(1 mark)*

H I N T
You can also use the formula $v^2 = u^2 + 2as$ with the same result.

(ii) For v you can now use $v = u + at$

giving $v = 2.71 \times 9.81$ *(1 mark)*

$= 26.6 \, \mathrm{m\,s^{-1}}$ *(1 mark)*

(c) The above, of course, assumes that there is no resistance and that the acceleration is constant at $9.81 \, \mathrm{m\,s^{-2}}$.

(i) Diver weight $= mg$

$= 61 \times 9.81 = 598 \, \mathrm{N}$ *(1 mark)*

(ii) At the terminal speed the force of air resistance equals the diver's weight, in magnitude.   *(1 mark)*

(iii) kv^2 is a force and so has units of newtons. Consequently k must have

units of $\dfrac{\text{newtons}}{(\text{m/s})^2}$

(This may be enough, but you can simplify down to the **base** units.)

But 1 newton is actually $1 \, \mathrm{kg} \, \dfrac{\mathrm{m}}{\mathrm{s^2}}$ (It is the force to accelerate 1 kg at $1 \, \mathrm{m\,s^{-2}}$)

So k has units $\mathrm{kg} \, \dfrac{\mathrm{m}}{\mathrm{s^2}} \, \dfrac{\mathrm{s^2}}{\mathrm{m^2}}$ or $\mathrm{kg\,m^{-1}}$ *(1 mark)*

As far as the magnitude of k is concerned, we have:

$kv^2 = 598 \, \mathrm{N}$

where $v = 90 \, \mathrm{m\,s^{-1}}$

so $k = \dfrac{598}{90 \times 90} = 0.074$

$k = 0.074 \, \mathrm{kg\,m\,s^{-1}}$ *(1 mark)*

(d) (i) At $25 \, \mathrm{m\,s^{-1}}$ the air resistance force $= kv^2$ *(1 mark)*

$= 0.074 \times 25 \times 25$

$= 46.2 \, \mathrm{N}$ *(1 mark)*

(ii) Thus in (b) at the maximum speed the air resistance is $\frac{46}{598} \times 100\%$
$= 7.7\%$ of the diver's weight.
Because the resistive force increases only with the **square** of the speed this means that the answers to (d) are valid to within at least 10%.   *(1 mark)*

Question 4 – Student's answer
See student's answer at the end of this section.

Question 5
(a) (i) Using the $m_1u_1 + m_2u_2 = m_1v_1 + m_2v_2$ formula, and taking velocities as positive when from left to right, we have   *(1 mark)*

$0.3 \times 0.2 - 0.2 \times 0.5 = -0.3 \times 0.2 + 0.2 \times v_2$ *(1 mark)*

giving $v_2 = 0.1 \, \mathrm{m\,s^{-1}}$

i.e. a speed of $0.1 \, \mathrm{m\,s^{-1}}$ from *left to right*   *(1 mark)*

(ii) The nett external forces acting must be zero.   *(2 marks)*

(b) (i) A perfectly elastic collision is one in which none of the kinetic energy of the colliding objects is converted into internal energy. An inelastic collision is one where some energy is converted into internal energy.

(1 mark)

Examiner's note This implies a temperature rise. Do not call it heat.

(ii) To show the collision is inelastic compute the total kinetic energy before and after.

$$k.e.\ before = \tfrac{1}{2}m_1u_1^2 + \tfrac{1}{2}m_2u_2^2$$
$$= \tfrac{1}{2} \times 0.3 \times (0.2)^2 + \tfrac{1}{2} \times (0.2) \times (0.5)^2$$
$$= 6 \times 10^{-3} + 2.5 \times 10^{-2} = 3.1 \times 10^{-2}\,\text{J}$$

$$k.e.\ after = \tfrac{1}{2}m_1v_1^2 + \tfrac{1}{2}m_2v_2^2$$
$$= \tfrac{1}{2} \times 0.3 \times (0.2)^2 + \tfrac{1}{2} \times 0.2 \times (0.1)^2$$
$$= 6 \times 10^{-3} + 1 \times 10^{-3} = 7 \times 10^{-3}\,\text{J}$$

showing a loss in k.e. *(1 mark)*

(iii) An example of a perfectly elastic collision is that between two molecules. *(1 mark)*

(c) (i) We use $m_1u_1 + m_2u_2 = m_1v_1 + m_2v_2$ and recognise that the speeds of the bullet and the block v_1 and v_2, after the collision, are the same. But before we can proceed we need to calculate v_1 which we can do from conservation of energy considerations recognising that as the bullet/block mass rises, there is conversion of the k.e. of motion $\tfrac{1}{2}(m_1 + m_2)v_1^2$ to p.e. (*mgh*). *(1 mark)*

Thus $\tfrac{1}{2}(1.99 + 0.01)v_1^2 = (1.99 + 0.01) \times 10 \times 0.15$ *(1 mark)*

giving $v_1^2 = 3$ and $v_1 = 1.73\,\text{m s}^{-1}$ *(1 mark)*

(ii) Using this in the momentum equation we get

$0.01u_1 + 1.99 \times 0 = (1.99 + 0.01) \times 1.73$ *(1 mark)*

and $\qquad\qquad u_1 = 346.4\,\text{m s}^{-1}$ *(1 mark)*

(iii) The tension in the string is slightly increased by the increased mass contributed by the bullet. But once moving the block is travelling in a vertical circle and the new tension T_1 minus the weight must equal mv^2/r. Put another way, the tension must be bigger than the weight by mv^2/r. *(2 marks)*

Question 6

(a) Angular speed $= \dfrac{\text{angle moved}}{\text{time}}$

$$= 2\pi/(90 \times 60)$$
$$= 1.16 \times 10^{-3}\ \text{radians s}^{-1}$$ *(1 mark)*

(b) (i) Acceleration $= \omega^2 r$

$$r = 6400 + 300\,\text{km}$$

Hence $\omega^2 r = 1.353 \times 10^{-6} \times 6700 \times 10^3$ *(1 mark)*

$$= 9.07\,\text{m s}^{-2}$$ *(1 mark)*

Examiner's note Watch the units here: *r* must be in metres.

(ii) The centripetal force $= m\omega^2 r$ giving a force of 907 N. *(1 mark)*

(c) In a complete orbit and assuming no friction leading to a change in orbit there is:

    (i) no change in the magnitude of the momentum, but a steady change, through 360° or 2π radians, of its direction;   *(2 marks)*

    (ii) no change in its kinetic energy.   *(2 marks)*

> ***Examiner's note*** If there is friction there is loss in energy and the satellite moves to a lower orbit, i.e. one with a smaller radius.
>
> The inward centripetal force is mv^2/r and is equal to the gravitational inverse square law force $\dfrac{GMm}{r^2}$
>
> Comparing these two gives $\dfrac{1}{2}mv^2 = \dfrac{GMm}{2r}$
>
> So as r gets smaller the k.e. increases. Consequently both the magnitude of the momentum and the k.e. increase in one complete orbit.
>
> (If this appears to contradict the conservation of energy, remember that it is the loss of p.e. (GMm/r) which supplies the increased k.e.

Question 7

Rise in p.e. $= mgh = 55 \times 10 \times 3.6$

$$= 1980\,\text{J}$$

    (1 mark)

Rate of increase in p.e. $= \dfrac{1980}{1.8} = 1100\,\text{W}$ *(1 mark)*

so athlete's power $= 1.1\,\text{kW}$ *(1 mark)*

> ***Examiner's note*** By base units is meant fundamental units such as metres, seconds, etc.

Units of power are joules/second. 1 joule is the energy expended in exerting a force of 1 newton through 1 metre.

The units of power are, therefore, Nm/s   *(1 mark)*

so $\dfrac{\text{Power}}{\text{Weight}}$ has units of $\dfrac{\text{Nm}}{\text{Ns}} = \dfrac{\text{m}}{\text{s}}$ *(1 mark)*

i.e. the unit of velocity.

Here power to weight ratio is $\dfrac{1100}{55 \times 10} = 2\,\text{m s}^{-1}$ *(2 marks)*

Question 8

(a) (i) Drawing a graph and extrapolating to $x = 0$ we find initial k.e. $= 320\,\text{J}$.   *(1 mark)*

    (ii) The k.e. does not fall to zero until $x = 2.15\,\text{m}$ which is beyond the end of the ramp. So the skateboarder will reach it.   *(2 marks)*

(b) (i) If the skateboarder just gets to the top of the ramp the new graph is one parallel to the old one cutting the x-axis at $x = 1.6\,\text{m}$ and the vertical axis at 240 J.   *(3 marks)*

    (ii) So initial k.e., $\frac{1}{2}mv^2 = 240\,\text{J}$

with $m = 60\,\text{kg}$, this gives $v^2 = \dfrac{240 \times 2}{60}$

$v = \sqrt{8} = 2.8\,\text{m s}^{-1}$.   *(2 marks)*

(c) The graph is now non-linear. The rate at which k.e. is converted to p.e. increases towards the end of the ramp, viz

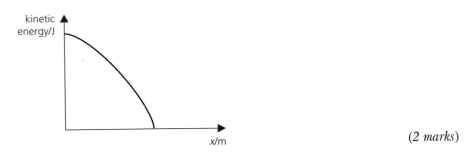

(2 marks)

Question 9

(a) The units of power are $\dfrac{\text{joules}}{\text{second}}$ and 1 joule is the work done when a force of 1 N acts through 1 m.

$$1\,\text{N} = 1\,\text{kg}\,\frac{\text{m}}{\text{s}^2}\ \ (\text{see Question 3})$$ *(1 mark)*

Hence the units of power are

$$1\,\text{kg}\cdot\frac{\text{m}}{\text{s}^2}\cdot\frac{\text{m}}{\text{s}} = 1\,\text{kg}\,\frac{\text{m}^2}{\text{s}^3}$$

The units of force are $\text{kg}\,\dfrac{\text{m}}{\text{s}^2}$, as above, and those of velocity are $\dfrac{\text{m}}{\text{s}}$

giving the units of Fv as $\text{kg}\,\dfrac{\text{m}^2}{\text{s}^3}$.   *(1 mark)*

(b) (i) On a level road all the energy used is to overcome the retarding forces. This is, therefore, 21 kW. Thus if F is the force of retardation,

$$Fv = 21 \times 10^3\,\text{W}$$ *(1 mark)*
$$v = 14\,\text{m s}^{-1}$$
Hence $F = 1.5\,\text{kN}$ *(1 mark)*

(ii) The extra power needed is equal to the increase in p.e. per second and is mgh where h is the height risen per second, h being found from the diagram below where $\tan\theta = \frac{1}{10}$.   *(1 mark)*

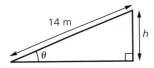

hence $h = 14 \sin\left(\tan^{-1}\frac{1}{10}\right)$
$$= 14 \sin(5.71°)$$
$$= 1.39\,\text{m/s}$$ *(1 mark)*

So extra power $= 900 \times 10 \times 1.39\,\text{W}$
$$= 12.51\,\text{kW}$$ *(1 mark)*

Total power needed $= 33.5\,\text{kW}$.   *(1 mark)*

(iii) Let the angle of the gradient by θ.

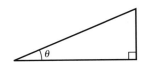

If the car coasts down without engine power the component of
weight down the gradient is $mg \sin \theta$.   *(1 mark)*
Hence $1500 = 900 \times 10 \times \sin \theta$
giving $\theta = 9.59°$ *(1 mark)*
$\tan \theta = 0.169$.
The gradient is therefore 1 in $1/\tan \theta = 1$ in 5.91.   *(1 mark)*

(iv) Retarding forces are usually not linearly dependent upon the speed.
In general the dependence on speed is a function of the kind
$F = a + bv + cv^2 + \ldots$ where the constants a, b and c need to be
known.   *(1 mark)*
Hence the retarding force cannot be calculated.   *(1 mark)*

Question 4 – Student's answer

(a) (i) Force is proportional to the rate of change of momentum.

> ***Examiner's note*** This is still not correct and complete: force is *equal* to the
> rate of change of momentum. Hence only 1 mark.

(ii) $F = m(v - u)/t$ giving $Ft = m(v - u)$
or $Ft = mv - mu$.

> ***Examiner's note*** Good: a standard piece of bookwork.

(iii) The dimensions of impulse are [Force] × [Time]

(iv) The impulse is the integration of force with time, and is equal to the total
change in momentum. So increasing the time of contact with the ball will
increase the momentum change, even if the force is not increased.

> ***Examiner's note*** Good answer.

(b) (i) Impulse = change in momentum
= mass × velocity
$= 0.60 \times 15 = 0.90$

> ***Examiner's note*** Arithmetic is correct: but don't forget the units, in this
> case Ns. One mark lost!

Average force = impulse/time $= 0.90/0.30 = 3\,\text{N}$

(ii) Horizontal velocity = 15 cos 60° = 7.5 m/s
Vertical velocity = 15 sin 60° = 12.99 m/s

> ***Examiner's note*** Correct: but make sure you can check that you have got
> sine and cos the right way round. As a check think of what it would be like
> if the ball went straight upwards at an angle of 90° to the ground. Would
> 15 × sin 90° give the right answer for the vertical speed? Yes, it would.

(iii) Use $v = u + at$ for the vertical motion.
$v = 0$
$u = 12.99$
$a = -9.81$
$t = ?$
Hence $t = 1.32\,\text{s}$

> ***Examiner's note*** Very good. But do you understand why you needed to
> neglect air resistance?

(iv) Use $v^2 = u^2 + 2as$ to find s the height risen.
Hence $s = (12.99)^2/(2 \times 9.81)$
$= 8.60\,\text{m}$

> ***Examiner's note*** You lose one mark for not remembering that the ball
> started 1 m above the ground. The complete answer is 9.60 m above the
> ground. Overall you understood the physics but made some careless slips.

2 D.C. circuits, resistance and capacitance

SOLUTIONS TO REVISION ACTIVITIES

1   (a) $A = 1.2 \times 10^{-7}\,\text{m}^2$ (b) $n = 8.5 \times 10^{28}$ (c) $v = 1.2 \times 10^{-3}\,\text{m s}^{-1}$

2   (a) $4.5\,\Omega$ (b) $1.3\,\text{A}$ (c) $4\,\text{V}$

3   (a) $50\,\Omega$ (b) $90.9\,\Omega$ (c) $99.9\,\Omega$

4   Use EIt, estimating I (say $0.3\,\text{A}$) and t (say $100\,\text{hrs} = 3.6 \times 10^5\,\text{s}$).

5

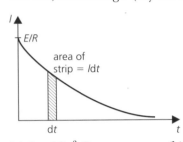
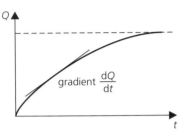

6   (a) $6 \times 10^{-3}\,\text{C}$ (b) $0.036\,\text{J}$

7   (a) $3 \times 10^{-3}\,\text{A}$ (b) $2\,\text{s}$ (c) $4.1 \times 10^{-4}\,\text{A}$ (d) $8.1 \times 10^{-4}\,\text{C}$ (e) $1.62\,\text{V}$

HINT

The total resistance of two resistors in parallel is always less than either, with the smaller resistance being dominant.

ANSWERS TO PRACTICE QUESTIONS

Question 1

Examiner's note The rate of flow of charge (the current) is the same through X and Y. Using the equation $I = nAev$, hence $v = I/nAe$, I (the current) is the same, n (the number of charge carriers per unit volume) is the same (same material), e (the charge on one carrier) is the same, A (the cross sectional area) is bigger in X and so v (the drift velocity) is less in X.

Answer   **B**   2 only

Question 2

Examiner's note Between **P** and **Q**, the resistance is $2\,\Omega$ in parallel with a series combination of $8\,\Omega$, $6\,\Omega$ and $4\,\Omega$. i.e. $2\,\Omega$ in parallel with $18\,\Omega$ (resistors in series add up). For resistors in parallel $1/\text{Total } R = 1/R_1 + 1/R_2$, hence Total $R = \frac{18}{10}\,\Omega = 1.8\,\Omega$
Between **Q** and **S** series combination of $2\,\Omega$ and $8\,\Omega$ in parallel with series combination of $4\,\Omega$ and $6\,\Omega$ i.e. $10\,\Omega$ in parallel with $10\,\Omega$, total $\frac{10}{2}\,\Omega = 5\,\Omega$
Between **R** and **S** $6\,\Omega$ in parallel with $8\,\Omega$, $2\,\Omega$, $4\,\Omega$ in series, total $= \frac{42}{10}\,\Omega = 4.2\,\Omega$
Between **S** and **P**, total $= \frac{24}{5}\,\Omega = 4.8\,\Omega$
Between **P** and **R**, total $= \frac{42}{10}\,\Omega = 4.2\,\Omega$.

Answer   **B**

Question 3

First compare the resistance of the new wire with the old wire using $R = \dfrac{\rho l}{A}$

New area $= 4A$ (area depends on r^2), so new resistance $= \dfrac{2\rho \times 2l}{4A} = R$

Hence new current is same as old current.

Answer   **B**

Question 4

(a) (i) When a p.d. of 4.5 V is applied across the lamp the power
converted $= 1.35$ W   *(1 mark)*

   (ii) Using power $= VI$, then $I = \dfrac{1.35}{4.5} = 0.3$ A and then

$$R = \frac{V}{I} = \frac{4.5}{0.3} = 15\,\Omega$$ *(2 marks)*

(b) The potential difference between X and Z is 6.0 V, which is divided in the
ratio of the resistors. Hence the p.d. across XY $= \dfrac{24}{24+8} \times 6.0 = 4.5$ V.
                                                                             (2 marks)

   Alternatively, using power $= V^2/R$, then $R = V^2/\text{power} = 4.52^2/1.35$
   $= 15\,\Omega$.

(c) (i) The resistance of the lamp is in parallel with the $24\,\Omega$ resistor, making
the resistance between Y and Z less than $24\,\Omega$, so the p.d. across YZ is
less than 4.5 V and so the lamp does not light fully.   *(2 marks)*

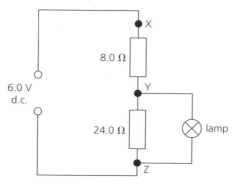

   (ii) The total resistance between Y and Z is now $\dfrac{1.5}{4.5} \times 8 = \frac{8}{3}\,\Omega$

   Using the formula $\dfrac{1}{24} + \dfrac{1}{R} = \dfrac{3}{8}$, hence $\dfrac{1}{R} = \dfrac{8}{24}$ and $R = 3\,\Omega$
                                                                             (2 marks)

   (iii) In (a)(ii) the resistance of the lamp was calculated with 4.5 V across
the lamp, whereas in (c)(ii) the p.d. was 1.5 V and so less current was
flowing through the bulb and so the resistance was less because the
bulb was colder.   *(1 mark)*

> **HINT**
>
> *With resistors in series the p.d.s are proportional to the resistances. The p.d. between Y and Z is now 1.5 V and so the p.d. between X and Y is 4.5 V.*

Question 5 – Student's answer

See student's answer at the end of this section.

Question 6

R and r are in series with a total of 12 V across them. Hence there will be 6 V
across R and 6 V across r if r and R are the same i.e. $R = 0.5\,\Omega$.

Answer   **B**

Question 7

When the switch is closed, C is uncharged and all the battery voltage V is
across R. Current I is a maximum $= \dfrac{V}{R}$. This current charges the capacitor
increasing the p.d. across C and decreasing the p.d. across R and so I is less.
This process continues until the p.d. across the capacitor $= V$, the p.d. across
$R = 0$ and $I = 0$.

Answer   **D**

Question 8

The p.d. across C + p.d. across R = battery voltage V at all times.

Answer   **A**

Question 9

(a) (i) If the p.d. across the capacitor is 1 V the charge stored $= 100\,\mu C$
(1 mark)

    (ii) $Q = CV$, so the charge $Q = 100 \times 10^{-6} \times 20 = 2 \times 10^{-3}\,C = 2\,mC$
(1 mark)

    (iii) $2\,mC$
(1 mark)

    (iv) Energy $= \frac{1}{2}QV = 0.5 \times 2 \times 10^{-3} \times 20 = 0.02\,J$
(2 marks)

        or $\frac{1}{2}CV^2 = 0.5 \times 100 \times 10^{-6} \times 20^2 = 0.02\,J$

(b) The maximum voltage is marked for safety reasons.
(1 mark)

(c) (i) $V_{out} = 6\,V$
(1 mark)

    (ii) $V_{out} = 0\,V$
(1 mark)

Question 10

(a) The $2\,\mu F$ and $6\,\mu F$ capacitors are in series with a combined capacitance C given by $\frac{1}{C} = \frac{1}{2} + \frac{1}{6}$, hence $C = 1.5\,\mu F$. This combination is in parallel with the $3\,\mu F$ giving a total capacitance $= 4.5\,\mu F$.
(3 marks)

(b) (i) The combined capacitance of $2\,\mu F$ and $6\,\mu F = 1.5\,\mu F$, which is less than $3\,\mu F$. If a p.d. is applied across XY the charge on the $3\,\mu F = 3 \times V$ (in μC) and on $1.5\,\mu F = 1.5 \times V$. Hence the $3\,\mu F$ capacitor stores most charge. (The $2\,\mu F$ and $6\,\mu F$ both store a charge of $1.5 \times V$).
(4 marks)

    (ii) $Q = CV = 3 \times 12 = 36\,\mu C$
(1 mark)

Question 5 – Student's answer

(a) (i) Current $I = \dfrac{V}{(R + r)}$
(1 mark)

        Examiner's note The student has correctly divided the e.m.f. by the total resistance.

    (ii) Power dissipated in $R = I^2 R$
(0 mark)

        Examiner's note A correct equation but the question asks for the answer in terms of V, r and R which is obtained by substitution from (i) power $= V^2 R/(R + r)^2$

    (iii) Total power $= VI$
(0 mark)

        Examiner's note Substitution gives total power $= V^2/(R + r)$

        Proportion $= \dfrac{I^2 R}{VI} = \dfrac{IR}{V} = \dfrac{R}{(R + r)}$
(1 mark)

(b) (i) $I = \frac{15}{16} = 0.94\,A$
(1 mark)

    (ii) Power $= 0.94^2 \times 8 = 7.0\,W$
(1 mark)

(c) $I = \frac{15}{24} = 0.63\,A$, power $= 0.63^2 \times 8 = 3.17\,W$
(1 mark)

    Examiner's note The current is correct but to calculate the power in both speakers the student should have multiplied by 2 to give 6.3 W.

(d) Less power dissipated in (c).
(0 mark)

    Examiner's note A comparison has been made but without comment. The student could have made a reference to the maximum power theorem, which states that the maximum power is dissipated when the resistance of the speaker = the internal resistance of the power supply.
The student has correctly recalled equations but has lost marks by not fully answering the question.

3 Waves and oscillations

SOLUTIONS TO REVISION ACTIVITIES

2 $x = A \cos \omega t$

$v = -A\omega \sin \omega t$

$a = -A\omega^2 \cos \omega t$

where $\omega = \sqrt{k/m}$, $T = 2\pi\sqrt{m/k}$ and $f = 1/T$.

ANSWERS TO PRACTICE QUESTIONS

Question 1

In spring-mass systems the period T is given by $T = 2\pi\sqrt{\dfrac{m}{k}}$ and the frequency f, is $\dfrac{1}{T} = \dfrac{1}{2\pi}\sqrt{k/m}$

i.e. proportional to $\sqrt{k}$.

Y has twice the stiffness (or k value) of **X**.
Therefore the frequencies are in the ratio $1 : \sqrt{2}$ giving answer **B**.

Question 2

> **Examiner's note** This is a question to test your real understanding of the SHM formulae, all of which are invariably given out with the exam paper.

In SHM $a = -\omega^2 x$
giving **A** as the correct answer.

Question 3

> **Examiner's note** By contrast this question tests your ability to manipulate the formulae given.

The kinetic energy $= \frac{1}{2}mv^2$ and this is also the total energy when the velocity is a minimum. Note that when this occurs the potential energy is zero.
In the notation of this question $v = a\omega \cos \omega t$ with a maximum value of $a\omega$
Hence maximum kinetic energy $= \frac{1}{2}ma^2\omega^2$

$T = \dfrac{2\pi}{\omega}$ and $f = 1/T$

Hence $\omega = 2\pi f$ and maximum kinetic energy $= \frac{1}{2}ma^2(2\pi)^2 f^2$

$$= 2\pi^2 ma^2 f^2 \text{ or answer } \mathbf{B}.$$

Question 4

> **Examiner's note** This question shows the kind of way your knowledge of SHM formulae will be tested in a modular examination. Compare it with Question **2** where **A** provides the graph needed. Don't forget to label the axes.

To use it to find T you need to have a formula for the gradient of the graph.
The formula describing the relationship between a and x is $a = -\omega^2 x$
Hence the gradient is $-\omega^2$

$T = \dfrac{2\pi}{\omega}$ and hence the period T is given by

$$T = \frac{2\pi}{\sqrt{\text{(magnitude of gradient)}}}$$

Note that to be sure of full marks you need to get as far as an explicit formula containing the gradient.

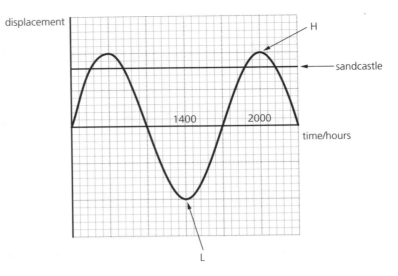

The graph has to be labelled as shown. Make sure that you recognise that the high tide to low tide time is *half* the period, and so is 6 hours. Equally remember that the amplitude of the graph is 25 m. Reading from the graph gives 1840 hours as the time the rising tide reaches the castle.

Note that this question requires very careful attention to be given to relabelling of the graphs and provides much scope for errors which carry through. The marking scheme is self-evident.

Question 5
See student's answer at the end of the section.

Question 6
(a) Two possible further standing wave patterns are as shown.

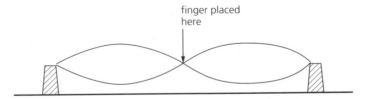

In this case the frequency is twice the fundamental frequency i.e. 560 Hz

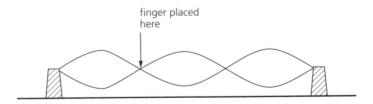

In this case the frequency is 3 × fundamental i.e. 840 Hz

(1 mark for diagram and 1 mark for frequency.)

Examiner's note A guitar string is normally pressed hard giving rise to a fundamental oscillation with nodes at the bridge and at the point of pressure.

(b) $c = \sqrt{T/\mu}$ c is also given by $c = f\lambda$ *(1 mark)*
Hence $f\lambda = \sqrt{T/\mu}$

$\lambda = 2l$ and hence $f = \dfrac{1}{2l}\sqrt{\dfrac{T}{\mu}}$ *(1 mark)*

(c) Let the new frequency be f' and the new tension be T'

Then $f = \dfrac{1}{2l}\sqrt{\dfrac{T}{\mu}}$ and $f' = \dfrac{1}{2l}\sqrt{\dfrac{T'}{\mu}}$ *(1 mark)*

Hence $\dfrac{f'}{f} = \sqrt{\dfrac{T'}{T}} = \sqrt{0.5}$

hence $f' = 197.9\,\text{Hz}$ *(1 mark)*

(d) (i) By saying strain reduction is 0.4% is meant that $\dfrac{\Delta x}{x} = \dfrac{-0.4}{100}$ where x is the length of a sample of the string.   *(1 mark)*

Hence the mass per unit length, proportional to x *increases* by the same amount i.e. $\dfrac{0.4}{100}$.

(2 marks: 1 for amount and 1 for saying increase)

(ii) Hence instead of $\dfrac{f'}{f} = \sqrt{\dfrac{T'}{T}}$ we have

$$\dfrac{f'}{f} = \sqrt{\dfrac{T'}{T} \cdot \dfrac{\mu}{1.004\mu}} = 197.9 \times 0.998$$

i.e. a frequency change of 0.02%   *(1 mark)*

Hence the frequency would be lower than that calculated, as the denominator in the square root expression is increased.   *(1 mark)*

Question 7

Examiner's note This question is of a type common to more than one board. Essentially you are given someone else's experimental results and either have to analyse them or else, as in this case, to comment on the data and how it can be used.

The values of $\sqrt{l}$ that the student would get for his/her graph are 0.31, 0.63, 0.84 and 1.00 $\text{m}^{1/2}$
i.e. they are not evenly spaced in $\text{m}^{1/2}$
It is for that reason that the l values are poorly chosen.   *(1 mark)*

$$T = \dfrac{2\pi\sqrt{l}}{\sqrt{g}} \quad \text{or} \quad T = \dfrac{2\pi}{\sqrt{g}} \cdot \sqrt{l}$$

This is a straight line graph of the form $y = mx$

i.e. the slope m is $\dfrac{2\pi}{\sqrt{g}}$

hence $\sqrt{g} = \dfrac{2\pi}{m}$ or $g = \dfrac{4\pi^2}{m^2}$ *(1 mark)*

So the student would find the slope m of the graph and insert it in the above formulae.   *(1 mark)*

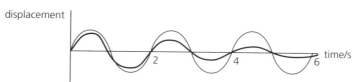

Taking g as $9.81\,\mathrm{m\,s^{-2}}$ and $l = 1\,\mathrm{m}$

$$T = 2\pi\sqrt{\frac{1}{9.81}} = 2.006\,\mathrm{s}.$$

The damped graph is as shown. The peak values diminish exponentially and the frequency is very slightly increased as a result of the damping.

Examiner's note In practice with very light damping the change in frequency will be almost imperceptible.)

(*Marks: 2 for putting in x-values, 1 for showing exponential fall in amplitude and 1 for showing no observable change in period.*)

Question 8
Examiner's note A phase difference has to be measured in degrees or radians. Hence both **A** and **B** are invalid answers. **Y** leads **X** and so the correct answer is **D**.

Question 9
(a)

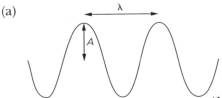

(*Marks: 1 each for amplitude and wavelength.*)

λ is the wavelength and A is the amplitude.

(b) (i) This is because as the progressive waves travel towards each end they are inverted and reflected. Thus the system experiences two travelling waves of the same frequency and wavelength, but travelling in opposite directions. The nett effect of two such travelling waves is a standing wave. The only wavelengths which are permitted are those for which there are nodes at the ends, as these points are fixed and have to be constant zero displacement. (*2 marks*)

   (ii)   **Examiner's note** It is useful to understand the difference between overtones and harmonics.

The first harmonic is the lowest frequency of vibration. The 2nd harmonic is the next highest frequency that can be present. So the third harmonic is as shown.

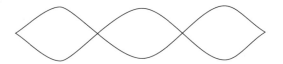

(*2 marks*)

   (iii) $f_2 = 2f_1$
The frequency of the second harmonic is twice that of the first.
(*1 mark*)
The speed of waves in the system is constant. (*1 mark*)
Thus as the wavelength is halved the frequency must double.
(*1 mark*)
Musically the second harmonic is an octave higher than the first.

Question 10
The incorrect statement is **C**.

Question 11

Examiner's note This question tests your knowledge of a typical wavelength of light. You will probably recall that the wavelength of visible sodium light is 5.89×10^{-7} m

Hence for sodium light $n = \dfrac{1}{5.89 \times 10^{-7}}$

$$= 1.70 \times 10^6$$

So the best value for n is **A**.

Question 12

The distance between the position of two wavefronts on the wall is found from geometry as $\sqrt{2 \times 20^2} = 28.28$ m. So two points 28.28 m apart would be out of phase by 360°. Consequently two points 10 m apart would be out of phase by $360° \times 10/28.28$ m or 127.28° giving answer **E**.

Question 13

(a) (i) If the received intensity is a maximum it means the transmitter signal and the received signal are in phase. If the plate is moved 7.5 mm to a point where the signal is a minimum it means that the received signal and that of the transmitter are now in antiphase. This is a result of the signal at the receiver travelling half a wavelength, λ, less, or M having moved by $\lambda/4$. *(2 marks)*

   (ii) The minimum is not necessarily zero because the amplitudes of the two signals at the receiver are not necessarily the same. *(1 mark)*

(b) If the plate moved at 7.5 mm/sec the signal would go from a maximum to a minimum in 1 second, and would go through a cycle of max–min–max in 2 seconds. Hence it would fluctuate at 0.5 Hz. Hence if fluctuating at 2.0 kHz *(1 mark)*

the speed is $\dfrac{7.5 \times 2.0 \times 10^3 \, \text{mm s}^{-1}}{0.5}$ *(1 mark)*

$$= \frac{7.5 \times 2.0 \times 10^3 \times 10^{-3} \, \text{m s}^{-1}}{0.5}$$

$$= 30 \, \text{m s}^{-1} \qquad\qquad (1 \; mark)$$

(c) When the fluctuating signal is 1 kHz the speed is 15 m s^{-1}. Assuming uniform deceleration and using the formulae of Longman Reference Guide page 32 we have

$u = 30 \, \text{m s}^{-1} \qquad v = 15 \, \text{m s}^{-1} \qquad s = 100 \, \text{m}$

so that using $v^2 = u^2 + 2as$ we have $a = -3.375 \, \text{m s}^{-2}$ *(2 marks)*

The braking force is given by $F = ma$ and so is 1200×3.375 N $= 4.05$ kN. *(1 mark)*

Question 14

Examiner's note This question compares with the travelling wave condition of Question **12**. As P and Q are both nodes, the situation is that all points between P and Q are in phase. The maximum amplitude is at R. As S and T are equidistant from R they will have equal amplitudes giving answer **A**.

Question 15

Examiner's note Essentially this is a Young's slit arrangement. The correct answer is **C**. **A** and **B** will increase the distance between points where the sound is loud. **D** will increase the loudness of the sound but will not effect the loud/quiet spacing.

Question 16

Examiner's note Some boards will set geometrical optics questions like this one.

(a) The required diagram is as shown.

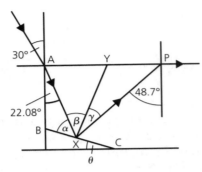

(*Marks: 1 for each place where the ray changes direction.*)

(b) (i) The required angle of refraction r is given by $\dfrac{\sin 30°}{\sin r} = 1.33$

Hence $\sin r = 0.375$ and $r = 22.08°$ (*1 mark*)

(ii) The critical angle c is given by

$\dfrac{1}{\sin c} = 1.33$ (*1 mark*)

giving $c = 48.7°$ (*1 mark*)

(c) *Examiner's note* To calculate θ for part (c) it is useful to draw in XY, the normal to the mirror at X, and to label the points and angles as shown.

As XY is a normal to the mirror, angle $ABX = 90° + \theta$

Hence in a triangle ABX $180° = \alpha + 22.08° + (90° + \theta)$

Hence $\alpha = 90° - 22.08° - \theta$

$\alpha + \beta = 90°$ and so $\beta = 22.08° + \theta$

$\gamma = \beta$ by the law of reflection.   (*1 mark for this or the diagram*)

angle $XYP = 90° + \theta$ and angle $YPX = 90° - 48.7°$,

so in triangle XYP we have $180° = (22.08° + \theta) + (90° + \theta) + (90° - 48.7°)$

So $22.08° + 2\theta = 48.7°$

Hence $\theta = 13.3°$.   (*1 mark*)

Question 5 – Student's answer

(a) SHM requires only a restoring force, proportional to the displacement, but acting backwards towards the point of equilibrium.

Examiner's note Good, if a little clumsily phrased. Emphasise that the force is proportional to the displacement *from the equilibrium position*. 1 mark for the proportionality and 1 for saying it is directed towards the equilibrium position.

(b) (i) Three complete cycles are executed in 2 s.

Hence the period $T = \frac{2}{3}$ s and the frequency $f = \dfrac{1}{T} = \frac{3}{2}$ Hz $= 1.5$ Hz.

The amplitude is 0.3 m.

Examiner's note The frequency calculation is correct but the common mistake of thinking of amplitude as a peak-to-peak distance has been made. There are probably 2 marks for this section and you have lost one.

(iii) $a = -\omega^2 x$ Consequently the maximum acceleration occurs at the maximum value of the displacement x, i.e. at $x = 0.15\,m$.

$$T = \frac{2\pi}{\omega} \text{ so that } \omega = \frac{2\pi}{T} = 2\pi f = 2\pi \times 1.5$$

hence $a_{max} = 4\pi^2 (1.5)^2 \times 0.15 = 13.3\,m\,s^{-2}$

Examiner's note You have used the correct value of amplitude in the calculation. Had you put in the wrong value the examiner would have had to have worked hard to see whether in all other respects your calculation was correct and to have rewarded you appropriately.

Well done. Two marks.

(iii)

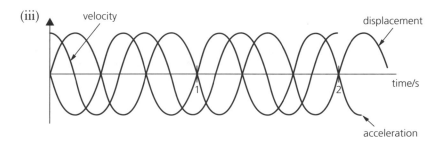

Examiner's note Note that the velocity is the slope of the displacement graph and the acceleration is simply an inversion of the displacement graph. Note that the question asks for labelled graphs, so you need to mark the maximum and minimum values of velocity and acceleration. The maximum and minimum values of the acceleration are $\pm 13.3\,m\,s^{-2}$ as already calculated. If the displacement is given by $x = x_0 \cos \omega t$, the velocity is $v = -x_0 \omega \sin \omega t$ with a maximum and minimum value of $\pm x_0 \omega$ or $\pm 0.15 \times 2\pi \times 1.5 = \pm 1.41\,m\,s^{-1}$

These values should be marked on the graphs. You forgot to do this and so you lose at least one of the probable two marks in total. In addition the questions says *graphs* and you have provided everything on one graph. This makes it difficult for you to answer the question and the examiner to fairly mark it. Overall quite a good answer, but see how silly slips or omissions can stop you reaching your capability.

4

Radioactivity and photoelectric effect

SOLUTIONS TO REVISION ACTIVITIES

HINT
235 g is the mass of *6×10^{23} atoms.*

HINT
5 MeV = 5 × 1.6 × 10^{-13} J

2   2.75×10^{24}

3   $9.6 \times 10^{-11}\,W$

4   $2.2 \times 10^{-11}\,s^{-1}$.

5 $\frac{dN}{dt} = -\lambda N = \frac{-N\ln 2}{t_{1/2}}$ i.e. activity depends on ratio $\frac{N}{t_{1/2}}$. The number of atoms depends on *both* the mass of radioactive material and the nucleon (atomic mass) number. Remember ^{60}Co means that there are 6×10^{23} atoms in 60 g and so the number of atoms in $100\,g = 100 \times 6 \times 10^{23}/60$. Similarly there are $100 \times 6 \times 10^{23}/90$ atoms in 100 g of ^{90}Sr. Hence the ratio $N/t_{1/2}$ is bigger for ^{60}Co

Answer **B**

6 Energy $= \frac{hc}{\lambda} = 3.3 \times 10^{-19}$ J

7 3.0×10^{26}

8 $\lambda = \frac{h}{mv} = 1.2 \times 10^{-10}$ m

> **HINT**
> energy/second = number of photons/second × energy of each photon.

ANSWERS TO PRACTICE QUESTIONS

Question 1

Initial activity is 100 Bq, so after 20 hours activity would be 50 Bq, eliminating answers **C**, **D** and **E**. Being an exponential change the count rate does not halve after a quarter of a half life and so the answer is **A**.

> **Examiner's note** There is no simple way to calculate the exact count for times which are not multiples of 1 half-life. After 10 hours the count is not 75 Bq because the count rate decreases at a slower and slower rate. The exact count rate at any time t is given by the equation $\frac{dN}{dt} = \frac{dN_0}{dt}e^{-\lambda t}$ where $\lambda = \frac{\ln 2}{t_2}$ so $\frac{dN}{dt} = \frac{dN_0}{dt}e^{-(\ln 2)t/t_{1/2}}$.
> Hence after 5 hours $\frac{dN}{dt} = 100e^{-(\ln 2)5/20} = 100 \times 0.84 = 84$ Bq.
> After 10 hours the count rate $= \frac{dN}{dt} = 100 \times e^{-(\ln 2)10/20} = 70.7$ Bq

Question 2

The emission of an α causes the atomic (proton) number to fall by 2 and the mass (nucleon) number by 4. A β *increases* the atomic number by 1 but does not affect the mass number.

Three alpha-particles emitted means mass number falls by 12 and so started at 219. The loss of 3 alpha-particles means the atomic number falls 6 *and* two beta-particles means the atomic number is up 2 so overall the atomic number is down 4 from 86.

Answer **B**

> **HINT**
> It is easier to calculate the new mass number first.

Question 3

(a) (i) After 4 half-lives the activity has fallen to $\frac{1}{16}$ (or $1/2^4$) of the initial value, i.e. the activity has fallen to $\frac{4.3 \times 10^5}{16} = 2.68 \times 10^4$ Bq
(2 marks)

(ii) The number of undecayed atoms is $\frac{7.9 \times 10^{15}}{16} = 4.93 \times 10^{14}$
(2 marks)

(b) $\frac{dN}{dt} = -\lambda N$. So $4.3 \times 10^5 = \lambda \times 7.9 \times 10^{15}$ *(2 marks)*

$\lambda = 4.3 \times 10^5/7.9 \times 10^{15} = 5.44 \times 10^{-11}\,s^{-1}$ *(1 mark)*

(c) The half-life $t_{1/2} = \frac{\ln 2}{\lambda} = \frac{\ln 2}{5.44 \times 10^{-11}} = 1.27 \times 10^{10}$ s *(2 marks)*

> **HINT**
> Not only does the activity fall exponentially but so does the number of atoms remaining. Watch out for questions which ask about the total number of atoms which have decayed.

> **HINT**
> Units of λ are s^{-1} because $\lambda = \ln 2/t_{1/2}$

Question 4

(a) Because the decay is a random process.   *(1 mark)*
(b) Some of the emitted particles will miss the ratemeter.   *(1 mark)*
   The ratemeter will also detect background radiation.   *(1 mark)*
(c) From your best smooth fit curve, find the time for the count rate to half,
   ~ 30 s   *(4 marks)*

Question 5

(a) An activity of 150 kBq means that 150 000 α particles are being emitted
   per second.   *(2 marks)*
(b) The current in the wire at P is a flow of electrons (upwards on the
   diagram) through the structure of the wire, whereas the current in the air
   at Q is a flow of positive ions towards the middle and electrons towards
   the positive can. Note that a positive ion and an electron (an ion pair) are
   created by each ionisation and they move in opposite directions from that
   point.   *(3 marks)*
(c) (i) The voltmeter is recording the p.d. across the $10^9\,\Omega$ resistor.

$$\text{Hence the current} = \frac{\text{p.d.}}{\text{resistance}} = \frac{3.4}{10^9} = 3.4 \times 10^{-9}\,\text{A} \qquad \textit{(2 marks)}$$

   (ii) A current of $3.4 \times 10^{-9}\,A = 3.4 \times 10^{-9}\,\text{C\,s}^{-1}$. Each charge carrier
       carries a charge of $1.6 \times 10^{-19}\,\text{C}$, and so the number of ionisations

$$\text{per second} = \frac{3.4 \times 10^{-9}}{1.6 \times 10^{-19}} = 2.1 \times 10^{10}. \qquad \textit{(2 marks)}$$

   This assumes that none of the positive ions and electrons *recombine* to
   produce a neutral atom.   *(1 mark)*
(d) The insulator is not perfect and a small current flows through it. A small
   current flows through the voltmeter itself.   *(2 marks)*
(e) The decay constant $\lambda = \dfrac{\ln 2}{1600 \times 3 \times 10^7} = 1.37 \times 10^{-11}\,\text{s}^{-1}$ *(2 marks)*

Examiner's note The half-life must be in seconds. You will either be given the
number of seconds (3×10^7) in a year or you can calculate the number
$365 \times 24 \times 60 \times 60 = 3.15 \times 10^7$.

Activity $= -\lambda N$, Hence $150\,000 = \lambda N$ and

$$N = \frac{150\,000}{1.37 \times 10^{-11}} = 1.09 \times 10^{16}\,\text{Bq} \qquad \textit{(2 marks)}$$

Question 6

The electron in this level will require 10.4 eV of energy to escape. Hence the
ionisation energy $= 10.4\,\text{eV} = 10.4 \times 1.6 \times 10^{-19}\,\text{J} = 1.66 \times 10^{-18}\,\text{J}$ *(2 marks)*

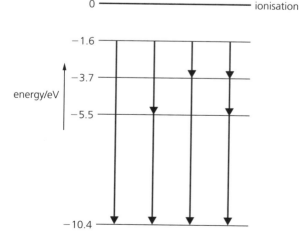

(3 marks)

$$\text{Energy of photon} = hf = \frac{hc}{\lambda} = \frac{6.63 \times 10^{-34} \times 3 \times 10^8}{600 \times 10^{-9}} = 3.31 \times 10^{-19}\,\text{J}$$

(2 marks)

$$\text{Energy} = \frac{3.31 \times 10^{-19}}{1.6 \times 10^{-19}} = 2.07\,\text{eV}$$

(1 mark)

A photon of this energy will be emitted by an electron falling from the $-1.6\,\text{eV}$ level to the $-3.7\,\text{eV}$ level. *(1 mark)*

> **Examiner's note** A fall involving a greater energy change will result in a photon of more energy and hence a greater frequency and smaller wavelength (i.e. towards the blue end of the visible spectrum). You are expected to know the approximate range of visible wavelengths, from blue 4.5×10^{-7} m (450 nm) to red 6.5×10^{-7} m (650 nm), with yellow, used as the average wavelength for white light around 6.0×10^{-7} (600 nm).

Questions 7, 8 and 9

> **Examiner's note** Questions 7, 8 and 9 all test whether you really understand the photoelectric effect and what the formulae mean.

Questions 7 and 8

The important points here are that the energy of an individual photon $= hf$ and so depends on the frequency of the light. Increasing f will increase the *energy* of *each* photon. Increasing the *intensity* of the light increases the overall energy and so increases the *number* of photons emitted. The *max k.e.* of an emitted *photoelectron* depends on the *energy* of individual photons. The photoelectric *current* depends on the *number* of photoelectrons emitted which depends on the *number* of incident photons.

Question 7

Increasing the intensity increases the photoelectric current and with no intensity there is no current.

Answer **A**

Question 8

Increasing the intensity does not increase the energy of individual photons and max k.e. of the photoelectrons will remain constant.

Answer **D**

Question 9

Energy of a photon $= hf = \dfrac{hc}{\lambda}$ and hence energy is inversely proportional to the wavelength. As λ increases, energy decreases.

Answer **B**

Question 10

(a) (i) $\text{Energy of photon} = hf = \dfrac{hc}{\lambda} = \dfrac{6.63 \times 10^{-34} \times 3 \times 10^8}{450 \times 10^{-9}}$

$$= 4.42 \times 10^{-19}\,\text{J}$$ *(1 mark)*

(ii) Remember $25\,\mu\text{W} = 25 \times 10^{-6}\,\text{J s}^{-1}$

Hence the number of photons per sec $= \dfrac{25 \times 10^{-6}}{4.42 \times 10^{-19}} = 5.66 \times 10^{13}$

(1 mark)

(iii) 10% of these photons produce electrons, so the number of electrons produced per second $= 5.66 \times 10^{12}$.

The current $=$ number of electrons per second $\times$ charge on each

$$= 5.66 \times 10^{12} \times 1.6 \times 10^{-19} = 9.06 \times 10^{-7}\,\text{A}$$ *(2 marks)*

(b) A photoelectric current will flow if the energy of a photon is greater than the work function of the metal.

$$\text{Energy of a photon} = hf = \frac{hc}{\lambda} = \frac{6.63 \times 10^{-34} \times 3 \times 10^8}{600 \times 10^{-19}} = 3.31 \times 10^{-19}\,\text{J},$$

which is bigger than $3.0 \times 10^{-19}\,\text{J}$, the work function.   (*2 marks*)

Question 11 – Student's answer

(a) (i), (ii)

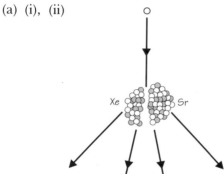

Examiner's note ^{139}Xe has more nucleons than ^{95}Sr, so the candidate has incorrectly labelled the Xe and Sr and has then *not* answered part (ii). You must make sure you answer all parts of the question.

(iii) Because a proton is positively charged.   (*1 mark*)

Examiner's note Make sure there is a complete explanation. It would have been better to add 'and so will be repelled by the positive uranium nucleus'.

(iv) $E = mc^2$, m before = 236.009, m after = 235.009
$$E = (0.201 \times 1.7 \times 10^{-27}) \times (3 \times 10^8)^2 = 3.08 \times 10^{-11}\,\text{J}$$ (*2 marks*)

Examiner's note The student has obtained the correct answer though m after should be 258.808. It would be clearer if more detail were included.

$$\text{e.g.} \quad m \text{ before} = 235.0 + 1.009 = 236.009\,\text{u}$$
$$m \text{ after} = 138.9 + 94.89 + 2(1.009) = 235.808\,\text{u}$$

In this part of the calculation you must use all the figures quoted. Remember to convert the mass to kg and remember to square the speed of light.

(b) (i) In 235 g are 6.0×10^{23} atoms

In 300 g are $\dfrac{300}{235} \times 6.0 \times 10^{23} \sim 8 \times 10^{23}$ atoms

Examiner's note Write down the calculated answer of 7.66×10^{23} and then add that this is approximately 8×10^{23}

(ii) The energy per fission $\sim 3 \times 10^{-11}\,\text{J}$,
total energy = $3 \times 10^{-11} \times 7.66 \times 10^{23} = 2.30 \times 10^{13}\,\text{J}$ (*2 marks*)

Examiner's note This part of the calculation can be done using the values given in the question and does not rely on you being able to do (a)(iv) or (b)(i).

(c) $750\,\text{kW} = 2.4 \times 10^{13}/x, \quad x = 3.2 \times 10^7$ seconds   (*1 mark*)

Examiner's note A correct calculation, but needs to make sure of full marks with a little explanation.
Overall the candidate seems to know what he is doing but a little carelessness and lack of detail can lead to unnecessary loss of marks.

5 *Electromagnetism*

SOLUTIONS TO REVISION ACTIVITIES

1

Magnetic field of current flowing
through straight wire

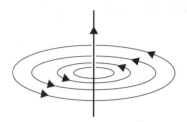

2 (a) 5×10^{-5} T   (b) 5×10^{-4} T
3 0.01 T
4 (a) 1.92×10^{-14} N   (b) 2.1×10^{16} m s^{-2} (c) 4.2×10^{-2} m $= 4.2$ cm
5 (a) 30 A   (b) 4500 W
6 7.07 V

ANSWERS TO PRACTICE QUESTIONS

Question 1

(a) (i) Use Fleming's Left Hand Rule. Hold the thumb, first finger and second finger at right angles. Point your second finger in the direction of the **c**urrent (direction XY on question paper), point your thumb in the direction of the force (**up**, the balance reading has decreased) and you will find that your **f**irst finger, representing the direction of the magnetic **f**ield, is pointing away from you, into the diagram in Fig. 5.2   (*2 marks*)

(ii) Using $F = BIL$, F is the force exerted on the wire shown by the decrease in balance reading but it is a *force* in N. The balance reading decreases by 35 g i.e. 0.035 kg corresponding to a force of 0.035×9.8 N $= 0.343$ N, $I = 2.0$ A, $L = 30 \times 10^{-3}$ m.

Hence $B = F/IL = \dfrac{0.343}{2.0 \times 3 \times 10^{-2}} = 5.71$ T   (*4 marks*)

(b) Use a calibrated Hall probe to measure the Hall voltage.   (*4 marks*)

Question 2

(a)

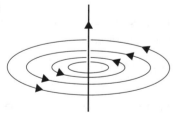

Magnetic field of current flowing
through straight wire

(*3 marks*)

(b) (i) Using the given equation $B = \dfrac{\mu_0 I}{2\pi a}$, substitute $a = r$ then $B = \dfrac{\mu_0 I}{2\pi r}$

(*1 mark*)

(ii) $F = BIL = \dfrac{\mu_0 I I l}{2\pi r} = \dfrac{\mu_0 I^2 l}{2\pi r}$ (*1 mark*)

(iii) The currents are in the same direction so the force is attractive i.e. towards R.

(1 mark)

> **Examiner's note** You can work this from a knowledge of the direction of the field due to the current in R and the use of Fleming's Left Hand Rule, but it is just as easy to remember that the force is **attractive** when the currents are in the **same** direction and that there is a mutual force of **repulsion** between the two wires when the currents are in **opposite** directions.

(iv) The same magnitude of force, i.e. $\dfrac{\mu_0 I^2 l}{2\pi r}$, but acting on R towards S.

(1 mark)

(c) (i) Using formula in (b)(iv) $F = \dfrac{4\pi \times 10^{-7} \times 5.0^2 \times 3.0}{2\pi \times 15 \times 10^{-3}} = 1.0 \times 10^{-3}\,\text{N}$

(1 mark)

> **Examiner's note** Each value is quoted in the question to 2 significant figures and so your answer should be to 2 significant figures. Note also that you can cancel π, but if you decide not to, be careful when entering the value of $\mu_0 (4\pi \times 10^{-7})$ into your calculator.

(ii) If one of the currents were reversed, the only effect would be that the direction of the force would be reversed.

(1 mark)

Question 3
See student's answer at the end of this section.

Questions 4 and 5

> **Examiner's note** Questions **4** and **5** both check whether you really understand the relevant formulae and what these formulae imply.

Question 4
Using the formula $B = \dfrac{\mu_0 N I}{L}$ the magnetic flux density B depends on $\dfrac{N}{L}$, but not on area nor resistance. Hence **1** only, answer **A**.

Question 5
$R = \dfrac{mv}{BQ}$, R decreases if Q increases, R increases if m increases and R increases if B decreases. Hence **2** and **3** only, answer **B**.

Question 6
(a) (i) Magnetic flux $\phi = BA$, where B is the magnetic field strength or flux density and A is the area perpendicular to the magnetic field.

(2 marks)

(ii) An e.m.f. is induced in coil Y when the magnetic flux in the core changes. Faraday's law states that the induced e.m.f. is equal to the rate of change of flux linking the coil.

(2 marks)

(b) (i) Assuming 100% efficiency the power generated in Y = power delivered to X. Hence $E_Y I_Y = E_X I_X$.

Thus $12 \times 3 = 240 \times I_X = \dfrac{36}{240} = 0.15\,\text{A}$

(2 marks)

(ii) The bulb would not light. An e.m.f. would not be induced in coil Y because the magnetic flux in the core would not be changing.

(2 marks)

HINT

You must give an explanation. Simply stating that transformers only work with a.c. will not give you full marks.

Question 7

Induced e.m.f. V = rate of change of flux linkage = $N \times$ rate of change of flux = $\dfrac{N\phi_{\max}}{t}$. Constant rate of change = change/time. Rearranging gives

$\phi_{\max} = \dfrac{Vt}{N}$.

Answer **D**.

Question 8

The relevant equation is $V - \dfrac{L\,\mathrm{d}I}{\mathrm{d}t} = IR$. V is the voltage applied to the coil and $-\dfrac{L\,\mathrm{d}I}{\mathrm{d}t}$ is the self induced 'back' e.m.f. At $t = 0$, the current $I = 0$ and hence $V = \dfrac{L\,\mathrm{d}I}{\mathrm{d}t}$ and so the rate of growth of current $\dfrac{\mathrm{d}I}{\mathrm{d}t} = \dfrac{V}{L}$. i.e. the bigger L, the smaller $\dfrac{\mathrm{d}I}{\mathrm{d}t}$. On the graphs, **A** has a bigger initial $\dfrac{\mathrm{d}I}{\mathrm{d}t}$, L_{A} is smaller and so $L_{\mathrm{A}} < L_{\mathrm{B}}$. The current stops increasing when $IR = V$ and $\dfrac{\mathrm{d}I}{\mathrm{d}t} = 0$.

Hence the maximum current is given by $I = \dfrac{V}{R}$. The bigger R, the smaller I. Hence $R_{\mathrm{A}} > R_{\mathrm{B}}$ because final $I_{\mathrm{A}} <$ final I_{B}.

Answer **A**.

Question 9

$E = -M\dfrac{\mathrm{d}I}{\mathrm{d}t}$, where $M = 20\,\mathrm{mH}$ and $\dfrac{\mathrm{d}I}{\mathrm{d}t} = \dfrac{\Delta I}{\Delta t}$. This is because the change takes place at a *constant* rate. ΔI is the change in $I(10.0\,\mathrm{A})$, and Δt is the corresponding change in $t(2.0\,\mathrm{s})$. Hence $E = 20 \times 10.0/2.0 = 100\,\mathrm{mV}$. The answer is in mV because the mutual inductance is in mH.

Answer **E**.

Question 3 – student's answer

(a) K.e. gained = electrical energy lost.

Hence $\tfrac{1}{2}Mv^2 = QV_o$, $\quad v^2 = \dfrac{2QV_o}{M}$ and $v = \sqrt{\dfrac{2QV_o}{M}}$ *(2 marks)*

Examiner's note If you are not sure whether electrical energy is lost or gained, first decide whether k.e. is lost or gained (k.e. is *gained* if the object is *speeding up*) and if k.e. is *gained*, *electrical energy* must be *lost* (conservation of energy).

(b) (i) left to right.   *(1 mark)*

    Examiner's note The direction of the electric field is the direction of the force it will exert on positive charge.

  (ii) Into the diagram. I used the left hand rule.   *(0 mark)*

    Examiner's note From (b)(i) The electric field force is to the right. If the ions are undeviated they must experience an equal and opposite force due to the magnetic field to the left. Use Fleming's Left Hand Rule, point thumb to the right, second finger downwards (direction of movement of positive charge) and your first finger will be pointing towards you, out of the plane of the diagram. You have incorrectly used the left hand rule and have made no comment about the forces balancing.

  (iii) The forces are equal.   *(1 mark)*

    Examiner's note The condition is that the force due to the electric field = force due to magnetic field. Your answer shows insufficient detail.

(iv) field $= \dfrac{V_1}{x}$ force $= \dfrac{V_1 Q}{x} = BQv$ $\dfrac{V_1}{x} = Bv$

$$v = \sqrt{\dfrac{2QV_o}{M}} \qquad V_1 x = B\sqrt{\dfrac{2QV_o}{M}} \qquad B = V_1/x\sqrt{\dfrac{M}{2QV_o}}$$ *(3 marks)*

(c) $F = BQv = \dfrac{mv^2}{R}$ *(2 marks)*

$$B = \dfrac{mv}{QR} = \dfrac{4.0 \times 10^{-26} \times 1.3 \times 10^5}{1.6 \times 10^{-19} \times 0.3} = 0.11\,\text{T}$$ *(2 marks)*

Examiner's note $R = 0.3\,\text{m}$ as the diameter is $0.6\,\text{m}$.

(d) (i) The force $= BQv$ and so as Q is doubled so the force will double   *(1 mark)*
      (ii) The diameter will halve.   *(1 mark)*

> **Examiner's note** $R = mv/BO$. Hence R and the diameter are halved if Q doubles. You clearly know and can use and manipulate equations but you do not always give full explanations.

6 Gravitational and electrical field and potential

SOLUTIONS TO REVISION ACTIVITIES

2 $1.65 \times 10^{-7}\,\text{N}$
3 $8.1 \times 10^{-4}\,\text{N}$
4 (a) $6 \times 10^4\,\text{Vm}^{-1}$ (b) $9.6 \times 10^{-15}\,\text{N}$
5 $9.81\,\text{Nkg}^{-1}$
6 (a) 24 hours $= 8.64 \times 10^4\,\text{s}$ (b) $4.2 \times 10^7\,\text{m}$
     (c) (i) $3.08 \times 10^3\,\text{m s}^{-1}$ (ii) $9.1 \times 10^{10}\,\text{J}$ (d) $1.6 \times 10^{11}\,\text{J}$

7 Escape velocity $v = \dfrac{2GM_E}{R_E} = 11\,200\,\text{m s}^{-1}$

8

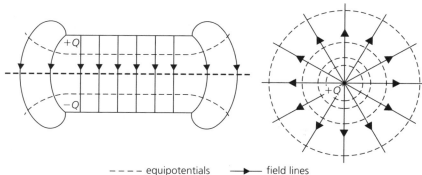

- - - - equipotentials   ⟶ field lines

ANSWERS TO PRACTICE QUESTIONS

Question 1

(a) (i) $F_E = \dfrac{e}{4\pi\varepsilon_0 r^2}$ where e is the charge on the electron and on the hydrogen nucleus (a proton) and r is the distance between the electron and the nucleus and ε_0 is the permittivity of free space.

(2 marks)

(ii) $F_G = \dfrac{GM_p M_S}{r^2}$ where M_p is the mass of the planet, M_S is the mass of the Sun, r is the distance between the Sun and the planet, and G is the Universal constant of gravitation. *(2 marks)*

(b) (i) Electrical potential is positive because there is a force of repulsion between a charge of $+1\,C$ and the hydrogen nucleus and so work needs to be done to move $+1\,C$ *from* a point a long way from the nucleus where the potential is zero. *(2 marks)*

(ii) Gravitational potential is negative because there is a force of attraction between the planet and the Sun and so work needs to be done to move the planet *to* a point a long way from the Sun where the potential is zero. *(2 marks)*

Question 2

See student's answer at the end of this section.

Question 3

(a)

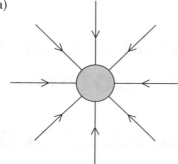

(2 marks)

(b) The field lines and equipotentials are perpendicular to each other.

(1 mark)

(c) (i) From P to Q it is moving along an equipotential and so there is *no* change in potential energy. *(2 marks)*

(ii) From Q to R the potential increases by $0.5\,MJkg^{-1}$, so the potential energy increases by $0.5 \times 3000 = 1500\,MJ$. *(2 marks)*

(d) (i) Work needs to be done to take $1\,kg$ from near to the planet to a long way away where the potential is zero. *(1 mark)*

(ii) The same work needs to be done to reach these points. *(1 mark)*

(iii) Where the field is weaker, further from the planet, to do the same work greater distances have to be travelled. *(2 marks)*

Question 4

(a) (i) The direction of the force is towards the positive (upper) plate.

(1 mark)

(ii) Field $= \dfrac{V}{d} = \dfrac{200}{5 \times 10^{-3}} = 4 \times 10^4\,Vm^{-1}$ *(1 mark)*

Force = field × charge = $4 \times 10^4 \times 1.6 \times 10^{-19} = 6.4 \times 10^{-15}\,N$

(1 mark)

(b) (i) The direction of the force vertically up, away from the nucleus.

(1 mark)

(ii) Force $= \dfrac{Q_1 Q_2}{4\pi\varepsilon_0 r^2}$

$= \dfrac{2 \times 1.6 \times 10^{-19} \times 2.4 \times 10^{-18}}{4\pi \times 8.8 \times 10^{-12} \times (2 \times 10^{-13})^2} = 0.17\,\text{N}$ *(2 marks)*

Question 5

(a) $F = ma$, so $\dfrac{GMm_s}{r^2} = \dfrac{m_s v^2}{r}$ and rearranging gives $v = \sqrt{\dfrac{GM}{r}}$ *(2 marks)*

(b) From (a) $M = \dfrac{v^2 r}{G} = \dfrac{17\,000^2 \times 1.4 \times 10^8}{6.7 \times 10^{-11}} = 6.04 \times 10^{26}\,\text{kg}$ *(2 marks)*

(c) Time $= \dfrac{\text{distance}}{\text{speed}} = \dfrac{2\pi r}{v} = \dfrac{2 \times \pi \times 1.4 \times 10^8}{17\,000} = 5.17 \times 10^4\,\text{s}$ *(2 marks)*

(d) Using $v = \sqrt{\dfrac{GM}{r}}$, speed $= \left(\dfrac{6.7 \times 10^{-11} \times 6.04 \times 10^{26}}{7.0 \times 10^7}\right)^{\frac{1}{2}} = 2.4 \times 10^4\,\text{m s}^{-1}$

(1 mark)

Question 6

Electric field depends on potential gradient.

Field $= \dfrac{-\Delta V}{\Delta x} = \dfrac{600}{5 \times 10^{-2}} = 12\,000\,\text{Vm}^{-1}$.

Force $=$ field $\times$ charge $= 12\,000 \times 2.0 \times 10^{-6} = 0.024\,\text{N}$.

Answer **B**.

Question 7

Field $= -\Delta V/\Delta x$. The gradient of the V against x graph is initially constant but negative, so the field is constant but positive, then the field is zero, then constant negative.

Answer **E**.

Question 2 – Student's answer

(a) (i)

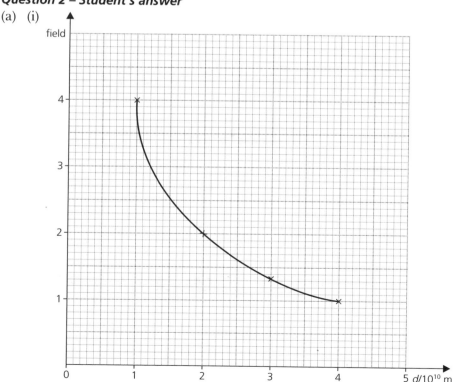

Examiner's note Unfortunately the student has incorrectly remembered the equation for field strength and has used field proportional to $1/d$.
The y-axis has been labelled but the units and powers of ten are missing. The incorrectly calculated points have been correctly plotted and a suitable smooth curve drawn. The field strength at the surface of the star is given $= 4.0 \times 10^3 \, \text{Nkg}^{-1}$, so the points to be plotted should be calculated using the inverse square law.

i.e.

Distance d/10^{10} m	Field strength/10^3 Nkg^{-1}
1.0	4.0
2.0	1.0
3.0	0.44
4.0	0.25
5.0	0.16

(ii) Field strength $= \dfrac{GM}{R} = \dfrac{6.7 \times 10^{-11} \times 5.6 \times 10^{33}}{4 \times 10^{17}} = 9.38 \times 10^{-5} \, \text{Nkg}^{-1}$

(0 mark)

Examiner's note Should be

$$= \dfrac{6.7 \times 10^{-11} \times 5.6 \times 10^{33}}{(4 \times 10^{17})^2} = 2.4 \times 10^{-12} \, \text{Nkg}^{-1}$$

(b) Force $=$ field strength $\times$ mass $= 9.38 \times 10^{-5} \times 2.0 \times 10^{30} = 1.876 \times 10^{36}$

(1 mark)

Examiner's note This is an e.c.f. (error carried forward), but the units are missing and there are too many significant figures. The student has correctly remembered the idea that force = field multiplied by mass. The correct answer $= 4.7 \times 10^{18} \, \text{N}$. Note that the answers should strictly be quoted to 2 significant figures because the values in the question are quoted to 2 significant figures. You must learn the equations you need to know.

7 Thermal physics and matter

SOLUTIONS TO REVISION ACTIVITIES

5 Assume a litre of water has a mass of 1 kg and that the specific heat capacity of water is $4200 \, \text{J kg}^{-1} \, \text{K}^{-1}$. Flow rate is 3.33 litres min^{-1}.

ANSWERS TO PRACTICE QUESTIONS

Question 1
Examiner's note This question is another example of one in which you analyse or comment on some experimental data. See also, for example, question 7 in Chapter 3.

(a)

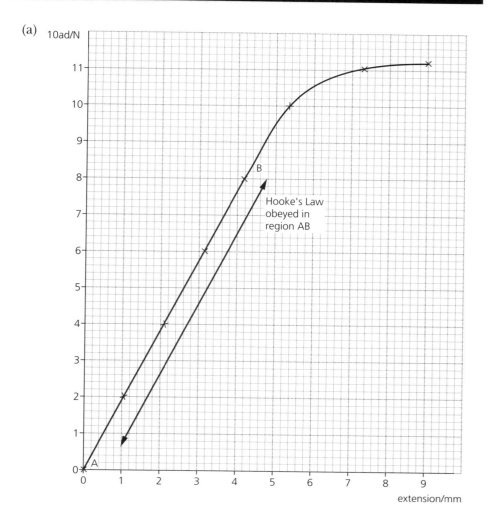

Marks are likely to be given as follows:

Correct plotting of points   (*1 mark*)

Appropriate scale   (*1 mark*)

Good line   (*1 mark*)

Labels and units set out   (*1 mark*)

Correct marking of the straight line region to indicate where Hooke's Law
is obeyed.   (*1 mark*)

(b) The slope of the linear part of the graph is $1.905 \times 10^3 \, \mathrm{N\,m^{-1}}$

Examiner's note It is useful to remember the Young modulus E as stress/strain.
Thus $E = (F/A) \div (x/l)$ where F is the applied force, A the area of cross section of
the wire, x the extension and l the original length.

$E = \dfrac{Fl}{Ax}$ which can be rewritten $E = \dfrac{F}{x} \cdot \dfrac{l}{A}$ (*1 mark*)

Note the units of E are, from this formula, $\mathrm{Nm^{-2}}$.
In this form we note that F/x is the slope of the graph, and so substituting
the value from the graph and values for A and l gives E.
Take care with units. If the wire diameter is 0.30 mm its radius r is
0.15 mm or 0.15×10^{-3} m.
A is given by πr^2 giving $\pi \times (0.15 \times 10^{-3})^2$ (*1 mark*)

Hence $E = \dfrac{1.905 \times 10^3 \times 1.5}{\pi \times (0.15 \times 10^{-3})^2} = 4.04 \times 10^{10} \, \mathrm{Nm^{-2}}$ (*2 marks*)

Question 2

This is a question involving use of the ideal gas equation $pV = nRT$. You should already be familiar with questions about changes of pressure, volume, and temperature to a fixed mass of gas, and where you use the equation

$\dfrac{p_1 V_1}{T_1} = \dfrac{p_2 V_2}{T_2}$. Here you employ the same technique by noting that

$\dfrac{p_1 V_1}{n_1 T_1} = R = \dfrac{p_2 V_2}{n_2 T_2}$. Hence to find the new pressure p_2 in terms of the old we

note that

$$\frac{p_2}{p_1} = \frac{V_1}{V_2} \cdot \frac{n_2}{n_1} \cdot \frac{T_2}{T_1}, \qquad \frac{V_1}{V_2} = \frac{V}{(V/3)} = 3, \qquad \frac{n_2}{n_1} = 3$$

Here note that an *additional* amount of gas, or number of moles, or number of molecules was added, tripling the initial amount.

$$\frac{T_2}{T_1} = \frac{T/3}{T} = \frac{1}{3}$$

Hence $\dfrac{p_2}{p_1} = 3 \times 3 \times \dfrac{1}{3} = \dfrac{1}{3}$ giving answer **A**.

Question 3

(a) The *root mean square (r.m.s.) speed* of gas molecules is the square root of the mean value of the molecular speeds

i.e. r.m.s. speed $= \sqrt{<c^2>} = \sqrt{\dfrac{(c_1{}^2 + c_2{}^2 + \ldots + c_N{}^2)}{N}}$

where $c_1, c_2, \ldots, c_N$ are the individual molecular speeds.   *(2 marks)*

(b) (i) The momenta add vectorially. The mean velocity is computed by a vector diagram.

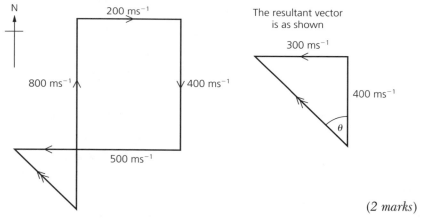

(2 marks)

HINT

Note the 3, 4, 5 triangle.

Using Pythagoras' theorem, the resultant vector is, $500\,\mathrm{m\,s^{-1}}$. The angle θ is $\tan^{-1} \frac{3}{4}$ or $36.8°$.

> **Examiner's note** Remember that the question asks for the momentum not the velocity, so we need to multiply the velocity by the particle mass.

Momentum $= 500 \times 5.2 \times 10^{-26}\,\mathrm{kg\,m\,s^{-1}}$

or $2.6 \times 10^{-23}\,\mathrm{kg\,m\,s^{-1}}$ at $36.8°$ west of north   *(2 marks)*

> **Examiner's note** For full marks it is necessary to specify the direction as well as the magnitude.

(ii) The mean kinetic energy is the mean of a scalar quantity. Hence we compute the k.e. of each molecule and then take the average. For the first molecule the k.e. is $\frac{1}{2} \times 5.2 \times 10^{-26} \times (800)^2$ J $= 1.66 \times 10^{-20}$ J The other kinetic energies are 1.04×10^{-21}, 4.16×10^{-21}, and 6.50×10^{-21} J,   (*2 marks*) giving a mean value of 7.07×10^{-21} J   (*1 mark*)

Question 4
See student's answer at the end of this section.

Question 5
(a) (i) The temperature of a perfect gas is proportional to the total kinetic energy of motion of the gas molecules.   (*1 mark*)

> **Examiner's note** The exact relationship between temperature and the kinetic energy is given by the formula
>
> $\frac{1}{2} Nm < c^2 >= \frac{3}{2} nRT$
>
> See Longman Revise Guide pages 242 and 243. Note also that for non-monatomic molecules, the total energy of the gas is not simply the kinetic energy of translational (or straight line) motion but is also the energy of rotation and vibration).

(ii) The internal energy of the gas is the total energy of the molecules of the gas.   (*1 mark*)
(b) (i) A shows the liquid cooling, B the steady change of liquid to solid without temperature change, and C the cooling of the liquid.   (*3 marks*)
(ii) At A the rate of loss of heat $\frac{dQ}{dt}$ is given by $mc_A \frac{d\theta}{dt}$ where m is the mass involved and c the specific heat capacity of the liquid. The rate of loss of heat depends upon the temperature above the surroundings and so is almost the same for A as for C (as the temperature at the AB junction is the same as at BC). At C $\frac{dQ}{dt} = mc_C \frac{d\theta}{dt}$ where c_C is the specific heat capacity of the solid. At B heat is lost at almost the same rate as in the adjacent regions of A and C, but without a change in temperature as the liquid gives up latent heat of fusion.   (*4 marks*)
(iii) Because the rate of loss of heat depends only upon the temperature above the surroundings and so is virtually the same for A (at the A/B boundary) and at C (at the B/C boundary)

$$ mc_A \frac{d\theta_A}{dt} = mc_C \frac{d\theta_C}{dt} $$ (*1 mark*)

So $\dfrac{c_A}{c_C} = \dfrac{d\theta_C}{dt} \Big/ \dfrac{d\theta_A}{dt}$

Therefore, because $\dfrac{d\theta_A}{dt} > \dfrac{d\theta_C}{dt}$, $c_C > c_A$ (*2 marks*)

Question 6
(a) Taking R as 8.32 J mol^{-1} K^{-1} and substituting the values for point B into the general gas equation in the form $n = pV/RT$ we get,   (*1 mark*)

$$ n = \frac{5.2 \times 10^5 \times 1.6 \times 10^{-4}}{8.32 \times 500} $$ (*1 mark*)

giving $n = 0.020$ moles.   (*1 mark*)

> **Examiner's note** The same could be done with either point A or point C.

(b) *Examiner's note* There is one mark for each of the seven answers required. We set out the working in full in order to help you.

Work done on gas for $A \to B = \int p\,dV$ (using the notation of the calculus) which is the area under the graph and is shown on the left.

Part 1 is $1.0 \times 10^5 \times (5.0 - 1.6) \times 10^{-4} = 34.0\,J$
Part 2 is $0.5 \times (5.2 - 1.0) \times 10^5 \times (5.0 - 1.6) \times 10^{-4} = 71.4\,J$
(using the fact that a triangle has half the area of the corresponding rectangle.)
Total work done is, therefore, $105.4\,J$.
By the first law, $\Delta Q = \Delta U + p\Delta V$ where ΔU is the increase in the internal energy.
Note that here work is done on the gas. The gas therefore does $-105.4\,J$ of work and so using the first law we get

$-22 = \Delta U - 105.4$ giving $\Delta U = 83.4\,J$

For $B \to C$ work is done by the gas as it expands and is given by the area under the graph $= (5.2 \times 10^5) \times (5 - 1.6) \times 10^{-4}$
$$= 176.8\,J$$
Thus the work done *on* the gas is $-176.8\,J$.
Using $\Delta Q = \Delta U + p\Delta V$
we get $618 = \Delta U + 176.8$
hence $\Delta U = 441.2\,J$.
For $C \to A$ we proceed differently. First we note that the gas has at the end gone in a complete cycle and that the *internal energy is only a function of temperature*. Consequently the increase in internal energy in going round the cycle from A to B to C must be equal to the loss of internal energy in going from C to A. Thus this must be a loss of $-(83.4 + 441.2)\,J$ or $-524.6\,J$.
Secondly, we note that as there is no change in volume, no work is done either by the gas or on it.
Thus $\Delta Q = \Delta U$ and ΔQ is also $-524.6\,J$.   *(7 marks in total)*

Question 7
Examiner's note The simplest way of tackling this problem is to call the interface temperature x and to recognise that dQ/dt, the rate of transfer of heat, equal to $kA\,d\theta/dx$, is the same for both sections of the rod. A is the same throughout.

For the left-hand section $kA\dfrac{d\theta}{dx} = 2kA\dfrac{(100 - x)}{2l}$

and for the right-hand section $kA\dfrac{d\theta}{dx} = kA\dfrac{(x - 0)}{l}$

Thus we get $2kA\dfrac{(100 - x)}{2l} = \dfrac{kAx}{l}$

or $\qquad\qquad 100 - x = x$

giving $\qquad\qquad 2x = 100,\ x = 50.$

Answer **C**.

Question 8
(a) For part (a) see your textbook.   *(3 marks)*
(b) *Examiner's note* To answer this question it is very helpful to draw a diagram.

(i) The temperature gradient in the ice is
$$\dfrac{0 - (-4.0)}{20 \times 10^{-3}}\ \dfrac{K}{m}$$ *(1 mark)*
$$= 200\,K\,m^{-1}$$ *(1 mark)*

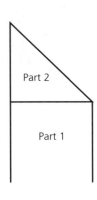

Part 2

Part 1

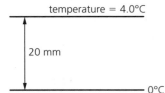

temperature = 4.0°C

20 mm

0°C

(ii) For $1\,\text{m}^2$ the rate of flow of heat $\dfrac{dQ}{dt} = \dfrac{k\,d\theta}{dx}$ *(1 mark)*

(A disappears from the formula as it is $1\,\text{m}^2$)

hence $\dfrac{dQ}{dt} = -2.1 \times 200$

$\qquad\qquad = -420\,\text{W}$ *(1 mark)*

Examiner's note The minus sign simply indicates that heat is lost *from* the ice.

(c) (i) The mass of additional ice formed = volume × density

$\qquad\qquad\qquad\qquad = A \times 1\,\text{mm} \times 910\,\text{kg}\,\text{m}^{-3}$

where $A = 1\,\text{m}^2$

Putting all units in SI form we get

mass $= 1 \times 10^{-3} \times 910\,\text{kg}$

$\qquad = 0.910\,\text{kg}$ *(1 mark)*

(ii) The energy removed from the water to form this is mL where L is the latent heat of fusion, *(1 mark)*

giving an energy of $0.910 \times 3.3 \times 10^5\,\text{J} = 3.003 \times 10^5\,\text{J}$ *(1 mark)*

(iii) As energy is removed at $420\,\text{J}\,\text{s}^{-1}$ the time taken is $715\,\text{s}$ or 11.9 minutes. *(1 mark)*

Question 9

The formula used assumes that between $0\,°\text{C}$ and $100\,°\text{C}$ as well as outside this range the temperature changes uniformly with voltage. Thus using

$\dfrac{X_t - X_0}{X_{100} - X_0} = \dfrac{t\,°\text{C}}{100}$ we obtain $t = \left(\dfrac{11.6 - 0}{4.1 - 0}\right) \times 100$ *(2 marks)*

$\qquad\qquad\qquad = 283\,°\text{C}$ *(1 mark)*

Question 10

Examiner's note For the definitions see *Longman Study Guide*. *(4 marks)*
The experiment which follows is an example of continuous flow calorimetry which relies on the fact that because the temperature above the surroundings is the same for both runs, the rate of loss of heat is the same, and can therefore be computed.

(i) Until a steady rate of flow is achieved the electrical energy supplies the heat losses from the apparatus, warms up the apparatus, and evaporates the liquid. Once a steady state is achieved we know that equilibrium has been established and that there is no further warming of the apparatus. *(1 mark)*

To confirm the constant rate of flow it would be necessary to collect several condensed samples of liquid over a fixed time interval, and check that they were the same in mass. *(1 mark)*

(ii) Let l_s be the specific latent heat of vaporisation of the liquid and P the rate of loss of heat from the apparatus. In the first experiment,
power supplied $= 5 \times 16 = 80\,\text{W}$,
power expended in vaporising liquid $= l_s \times 3.5 \times 10^{-5}\,\text{W}$,
so $80 = P + 3.5 \times 10^{-5}\,l_s$. *(2 marks)*
In the second experiment,
power supplied $= 7.5 \times 24 = 180\,\text{W}$,
power expended in vaporising liquid $= l_s \times 8.0 \times 10^{-5}\,\text{W}$,
so $180 = P + 8.0 \times 10^{-5}\,l_s$. *(2 marks)*
Subtracting the first of the final equations from the second gives us,
$100 = 4.5 \times 10^{-5}\,l_s$
$l_s = 2.22 \times 10^6\,\text{J}\,\text{kg}^{-1}$ *(2 marks)*

Question 11

(a) *Conduction*   Heat is transferred by collisions between the molecules. In the hotter region of the gas the root mean square speed of the molecules will be faster than in the cooler region. The random nature of the collision process will transfer this kinetic energy from the hotter region to the cooler. *(1 mark)*

Convection   Energy is transferred by the bulk movement of gas from the hotter region to the colder. *(1 mark)*

Radiation   The hotter region emits and absorbs radiation in the form of photons. Some of these will reach the cold region where the rate of emission and absorption is smaller. There will be a net absorption of photons in the colder region leading to a raise in the temperature there. At the hotter region the rate at which photons are emitted will not be balanced by the rate of absorption and the temperature will fall. *(2 marks)*

(b) **Examiner's note** This question is typical of the style of many questions on experimental methods, where detailed descriptions are not required, but where an understanding of the principles is necessary.

(i) Measurements needed:

1 Either the p.d., V, and current, I, in the heater (so that the rate of input of energy, $\dfrac{dQ}{dt}$, can be determined) or the rate of flow of cooling water and the ensuing temperature difference so that the rate of capture of energy from the cold end can be found. *(1 mark)*

2 The distance, x, between the two thermometers. *(1 mark)*

3 The temperature readings, θ_1 and θ_2, on the two thermometers. *(1 mark)*

4 The diameter d of the conductor. *(1 mark)*

These results are related by the equation:

$$\frac{dQ}{dt} = VI = k\pi \frac{d^2}{4} \frac{(\theta_1 - \theta_2)}{x} \qquad \textit{(1 mark)}$$

(ii) The experimenter must ensure that the cooling water runs at a steady rate and that V and I are constant, and he/she must wait for steady temperatures θ_1 and θ_2 to be obtained. *(2 marks)*

(iii) If the lagging were removed not all the heat entering on the left would arrive at the right, some escaping from the surface of the conductor. As a result θ_2 would be too low and the value of k would be too small. *(2 marks)*

(c) (i) Let the temperature at the cooler end of the aluminium rod be θ_2. In the usual notation, for the rod

$$\frac{dQ}{dt} = kA \frac{(\theta_1 - \theta_2)}{x}$$

where $A = 50\,\text{mm}^2 = 50 \times 10^{-6}\,\text{m}^2$

$\theta_1 = 80\,°\text{C}$,

$x = 20\,\text{mm} = 0.02\,\text{m}$

and $dQ/dt = 3.0\,\text{W}$

i.e. the rod must be conducting heat at 3.0 W.

This gives $3 = \dfrac{200 \times 50 \times 10^{-6}\,(80 - \theta_2)}{0.02}$ *(2 marks)*

making $(80 - \theta_2) = 6$,

so that $\theta_2 = 74\,°\text{C}$. *(1 mark)*

Assuming there is good contact with the rod the heat-sink is 54 K above the surroundings.

Let its area be A.

Then $90 \times A \times 54 = 3$ W, making $A = 6.17 \times 10^{-4}$ m^2, or 617 mm^2.

(2 marks)

(ii) If the heat sink does not make good contact with the rod the equilibrium temperature will be lower as there will be a temperature gradient across the interface. As a result a larger heat sink will be needed.

(2 marks)

Question 12

Examiner's note The principle used is that the energy supplied by the heater can only go to the air. From this it is possible to calculate the rate of flow of mass. In problems like this it is easier to consider what happens in 1 second.

(a) (i) Let m be the mass in kg of air flowing in 1 second.

The temperature rise is 40 degrees C.

Hence energy supplied per second, using the $mc(\theta_2 - \theta_1)$ formula, is $m \times 990 \times 40$ J, which must be equal to the energy delivered per second, which is 600 J.

(1 mark)

Thus $600 = m \times 990 \times 40$

giving $m = 0.015\,15$ kg s^{-1}

(1 mark)

i.e. a mass flow rate of 15.15 g s^{-1}

(1 mark)

(ii) As the density is 1.25 kg m^{-3} we can compute the volume per second.

Density = mass/volume, so volume = mass/density

(1 mark)

$= 0.012\,12$ m^3

i.e. a volume flow rate of 0.012 12 m^3 s^{-1} or 12 120 cm^3 s^{-1}

(1 mark)

(b) The second calculation is similar. The temperature rise is now 55 °C.

(1 mark)

For the mass flow we now have: $1200 = m \times 990 \times 55$

(1 mark)

giving a flow of 0.0220 kg s^{-1}

(1 mark)

(c) Without an increase in the volume flow rate the temperature of the air would rise by double the first rate, or 80 °C. Consequently if the ambient temperature is 20 °C the output temperature would be 100 °C.

(1 mark)

This would be dangerously high for a domestic device pointed at human skin. In addition, if there were any kind of accidental constriction of the opening of the dryer, the rate of flow could be diminished leading to higher interior temperatures which could damage the dryer itself.

(1 mark)

(d) Using $P = VI$ we have

$1200 = 241I$ giving

(1 mark)

$I = 5.0$ A.

(1 mark)

(e) (i) In natural convection, heat is carried away by fluids (air or gas) surrounding a hot object, which move away from the hot object as a result of a change in their density on being heated. In the case of forced convection the natural rate of flow of fluid around the hot object is increased by forcing a flow by a fan, pump or turbine.

(2 marks)

(ii) $\dfrac{d\theta}{dt} = -k(\theta - \theta_o)$

The equation says that the rate at which the temperature of the hot object falls $\left(-\dfrac{d\theta}{dt}\right)$ is proportional to the temperature difference between it (at temperature θ) and its surroundings (at temperature θ_o). k is the constant of proportionality.

(2 marks)

(iii) Using the equation to explain what happens to the hot air temperature is not straightforward. This is because the heater element, although constantly losing heat, never actually drops in temperature. Essentially it is in equilibrium and as fast as it loses energy it is replenished in energy by the electricity supply. In the formula $d\theta/dt$ is proportional to the rate of dissipation of energy. This is constant.

Thus $k(\theta - \theta_o)$ is constant, so if the hair dryer is used in colder conditions with a lower value of θ_o, θ is lowered by the same amount.

(2 marks)

Examiner's note This is the most difficult point of this question and you need to be very clear about the physical principles and to show that you understand them.

(f) If the fan were to stop working the rate of loss of heat from the element would rely on natural convection. Consequently the heating element would rise in temperature, possibly considerably and dangerously.

(2 marks)

Question 4 – Student's answer

The heat capacity of the water $= 0.500 \times 4200 \, \text{J K}^{-1}$
$$= 2100 \, \text{J K}^{-1}$$
and heat capacity of saucepan $= 1.20 \times 900$
$$= 1080 \, \text{J K}^{-1}$$
giving a total heat capacity, C, of 3180.

(2 marks)

Examiner's note Good, but one mark lost for omitting the unit in the final answer.

The rate of rise of temperature is $31/2.5$ degrees C per minute,
$$= 0.207 \, ^\circ\text{C s}^{-1}.$$

(0 marks)

Examiner's note There are two mistakes here. First the rate of temperature rise has been found by using the first two points on the graph. For full marks it is expected that a graph is drawn and then a tangent to the curve drawn at $t = 0$. Secondly there is a slip in reading the graph, which does not begin at zero temperature but at $20 \, ^\circ\text{C}$. The correct value is $4.66 \, ^\circ\text{C min}^{-1}$ or $0.0777 \, ^\circ\text{C s}^{-1}$.

The rate of supply of energy is equal to the total heat capacity multiplied by the rate of temperature rise, $C \dfrac{d\theta}{dt}$ giving 658 W.

(2 marks)

Examiner's note Here the answer is wrong because of the error carried forward. But this error would not be penalised twice. The correct answer is 247 W. Note here the importance of ensuring that all final values are in SI units. This ensures automatically that when values are multiplied together the computed value is also in SI units.

As the temperature of the water and saucepan rises above its surroundings the rate at which it loses heat increases. Thus while the rate at which heat is supplied is steady the rate at which heat is lost steadily increases and the nett rate of temperature rise slows down progressively.

(2 marks)

Examiner's note A good answer to complete the question.

Timed practice paper

Time allowed: $1\frac{1}{2}$ hours

Question 1

In the leisure pursuit called parascending a person attached to a parachute is towed over the sea by a tow-rope attached to a motor boat, as shown in Figure TP1.1

Figure TP1.1

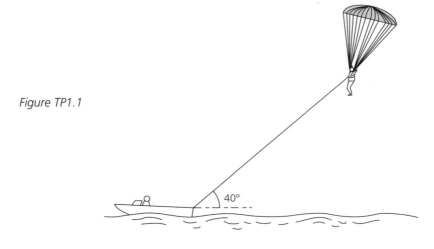

Figure TP1.2

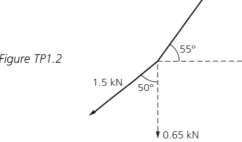

Figure TP1.2 shows the directions of the forces acting on a person of weight 0.55 kN when being towed horizontally at a constant speed of 8.5 m s^{-1}. The 1.5 kN force is the tension in the tow-rope and the force labelled **D** is the drag force.

(a) State why the resultant force on the person must be zero.

(b) Using a vector diagram, or otherwise, determine the magnitude of the drag force.

(c) (i) State the magnitude and direction of the force exerted by the tow-rope on the boat.

    (ii) Determine the horizontal resistance to motion of the boat produced by the tow-rope.

    (iii) The horizontal resistance to motion produced by the water is 1200 N. Determine the useful power developed by the boat's motor. (*8 marks*)

(AEB)

Question 2

(a) Figure TP2.1 shows a ray of monochromatic light travelling from a vacuum into perspex of refractive index 1.47.

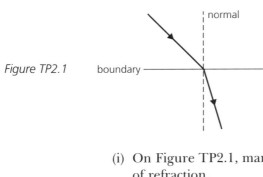

Figure TP2.1

(i) On Figure TP2.1, mark clearly the angle of incidence and the angle of refraction. *(2 marks)*

(ii) State Snell's law of refraction. *(2 marks)*

(iii) Calculate the angle of refraction when the angle of incidence is 50°. *(2 marks)*

(iv) Calculate the speed of light in perspex. *(2 marks)*

(v) Calculate the critical angle for light traversing the perspex-vacuum boundary. *(2 marks)*

(b) Figure TP2.2a shows the boundary between a vacuum and perspex. On Fig. TP2.2a, draw the path of a ray which strikes the boundary at an angle **greater than** the critical angle, so that the ray undergoes total internal reflection. Draw the path of the ray after it has struck the boundary. In the boxes in Fig. TP2.2a, identify the media.

Medium 1 is

Figure TP2.2a

Boundary _____

Medium 2 is

On Fig. TP2.2b, draw the path of another ray, incident in the same initial medium as in Fig. TP2.2a, and which strikes the boundary at an angle **equal to** the critical angle. Also draw the path of the ray after it has struck the boundary.

Medium 1

Figure TP2.2b

Boundary _____

Medium 2

Finally, on Fig. TP2.2c, draw the path of a third ray, incident in the same initial medium as in Fig. TP2.2a, and which strikes the boundary at an angle **less than** the critical angle. Also draw the path of the ray after it has struck the boundary.

Medium 1

Figure TP2.2c

Boundary _____

Medium 2 *(3 marks)*

(c) In a flexible endoscope, two bundles of optical fibres are normally used. One bundle is used to provide illumination, and the other to transmit an image.

(i) Describe the arrangement of fibres within the bundle used to transmit the image. *(2 marks)*

(ii) Explain why the fibres are arranged like this. *(1 mark)*

(NICCEA)

Question 3

A parallel beam of light from an illuminated vertical slit consists of one red wavelength and one blue wavelength. It is incident normally on a diffraction grating having 3.00×10^5 lines m^{-1} placed on a horizontal surface.

(a) The wavelength of the blue light is 450 nm.
    Calculate the angle between the straight through position and the first
    order maximum for this wavelength.   (2 marks)

(b) The diffracted light is observed as the angle from the straight through
    position is increased and the following lines are seen in sequence: blue,
    red, blue. Then a blue line and a red line are seen to coincide.
    (i)   Which order red line is the one which coincides?
    (ii) Calculate the wavelength of the red light.
    (iii) Calculate the angle at which the red and blue lines coincide.
                                                                          (5 marks)

(c) Diffracted light is observed at greater angles than in (b). At what other
    angle, if any, can a red line and a blue line be seen to coincide?   (2 marks)
                                                                           (NEAB)

Question 4

The circuit in Fig. TP4.1 is used to investigate the discharge of a capacitor.

Figure TP4.1

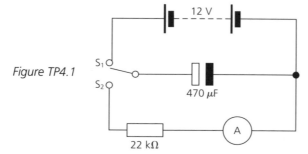

With the switch in position S_1 the capacitor is charged. The switch is then moved to S_2 and readings of current and time are taken as the capacitor discharges through the resistor. The results are plotted on the graph in Fig. TP4.2.

Figure TP4.2

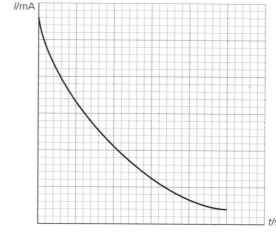

Calculate the maximum charge stored in the capacitor.

. . . .

. . . .

                                        Charge = ... (1 mark)

Make suitable calculations to enable you to add scales to both axes of the graph in Fig. TP4.2.

. . . .

. . . .

. . . .

. . . .

. . . . *(4 marks)*

A second $470\,\mu\text{F}$ capacitor is connected in series with the original capacitor.
The switch is moved back to S_1 to recharge the capacitors.
State the new charge stored.

. . . . *(1 mark)*

The switch is moved to S_2 and another set of discharge readings is taken.
Draw a second line on the graph to show how the current varies with time
during this discharge.   *(2 marks)*
How could the charge stored in the capacitors be estimated *from your graph*?

. . . .

. . . .

. . . . *(1 mark)*
(London)

Question 5
The graph in Fig. TP5.1 shows how the maximum kinetic energy (E_k) of an
electron emitted from the surface of potassium by the photoelectric effect
varies with the frequency f of the incident radiation.

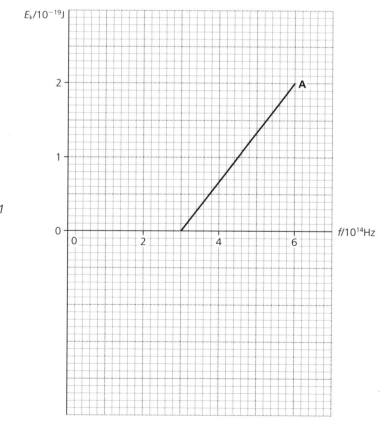

Figure TP5.1

(a) The maximum kinetic energy of the photoelectron is given by

$$(E_k)_{max} = hg - \Phi$$

    (i) State the significance of hf.
    (ii) Use the graph to determine a value for the Planck constant.
(b) Determine the minimum photon energy required to emit an electron. Give your answer in eV.

    Charge on an electron $= -1.6 \times 10^{-19}$ C.

(c) Sketch a copy of the graph labelling the given line **A**. On the same axes draw a second graph showing the result of using a material with a higher work function. Label this line **B**.   (*7 marks*)
            (AEB)

Question 6

Blood contains ions in solution. The diagram in Fig. TP6.1 shows a model used to demonstrate the principle of an electromagnetic flowmeter which is used to measure the rate of flow of blood through an artery.

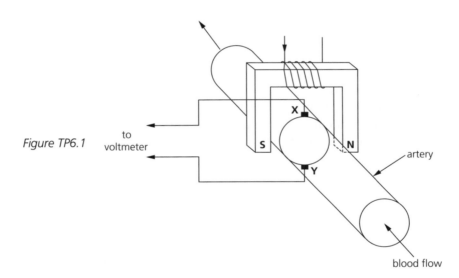

Figure TP6.1

When a magnetic field of 2.0 T is produced by the electromagnet, a potential difference (p.d.) of 600 μV is developed between the two electrodes **X** and **Y**. The cross-sectional area of the artery is 1.5×10^{-6} m^2. The separation of the electrodes is 1.4×10^{-3} m.

(a) Write down an expression for the force on an ion in the blood which is moving at right angles to the magnetic field, defining the symbols you use.

(b) An ion has a charge of 1.6×10^{-19} C.
    Show that the force on the ion due to the electric field between **X** and **Y** is 6.9×10^{-20} N.

(c) Given that a p.d. of 600 μV is developed when the electric and magnetic forces on an ion are equal and opposite, calculate:
    (i) the speed of the blood through the artery;
    (ii) the volume of blood flowing each second through the artery.

            (*8 marks*)
            (AEB)

Question 1

(a) The person is travelling at a constant speed. *(1 mark)*

(b)

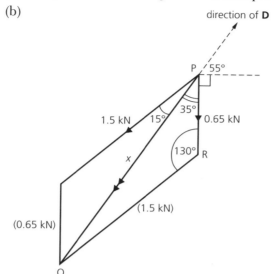

Examiner's note The magnitude of **D** is equal to the resultant of the 1.5 kN and 0.65 kN forces (see diagram above). There are several ways of computing the resultant. We shall use the cosine rule formula in triangle PQR.

$$x^2 = 0.65^2 + 1.5^2 - 2 \times 0.65 \times 1.5 \times \cos 130°$$
$$= 3.926$$

Hence $x = 1.98$ kN. *(3 marks)*

(c) (i) 1.5 kN at 40° to the horizontal. *(1 mark)*

   (ii) The required force is the horizontal component of the force in the tow rope,
   i.e. $1.5 \cos 40°$ kN $= 1.15$ kN. *(1 mark)*

   (iii) The total forces opposing the force of the motor are therefore
   $1.20 + 1.15$ kN $= 2.35$ kN. *(1 mark)*
   The power supplied = force × velocity $= 2.35 \times 10^3 \times 8.5$
   $= 19.97 \times 10^3$ W
   $= 20.0$ kW to 3 significant figures *(1 mark)*

Question 2

Examiner's note Some boards will set questions on geometrical optics like this one. Note that the last part about an endoscope will only be asked if endoscopes are in your syllabus. They are an interesting example of the use of total internal reflection in optical fibres.

(a) (i) and (ii) See Revision Tips. *(2 marks each)*

   (iii) $\dfrac{\sin 50°}{\sin r} = 1.47$

   Hence $\sin r = \dfrac{0.766}{1.47} = 0.521$ *(1 mark)*

   and $r = 31.4$ degrees. *(1 mark)*

   (iv) Speed of light $= 3.00 \times 10^8 / 1.47$ *(1 mark)*
   $= 2.04 \times 10^8$ m s^{-1} *(1 mark)*

   (v) $1/\sin c = 1.47$ *(1 mark)*
   hence $\sin c = 0.680$
   giving critical angle, $c = 42.8$ degrees *(1 mark)*

(b)

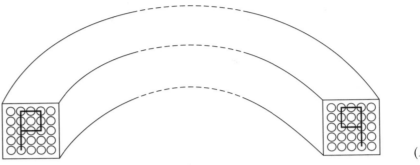

(3 marks)

(c) (i) The arrangement of fibres is as shown in the diagram:

Coherent bundle of fibres

(1 mark)

The fibres are located like a parallel set of railway tracks, and such that a cross section is arranged the same way wherever a section is taken. *(1 mark)*

(ii) The image falls on a certain number of fibres, and each one receives light forming part of the image. The fibres transmit this through to the opposite end of the bundle but only if the arrangement of fibres is the same throughout the bundle. *(1 mark)*

> **HINT**
> *A diagram is not asked for, but it is useful to sketch one if it helps the explanation.*

Question 3

(a) The formula for first order diffractions is $d \sin \theta = \lambda_B$

So $\sin \theta = \dfrac{\lambda_B}{d}$ *(1 mark)*

giving $\sin \theta = 450 \times 10^{-9} \times 3 \times 10^5 = 0.1350$
Hence $\theta = 7.75°$ *(1 mark)*

(b) (i) The coinciding red line is in second order. *(2 marks)*

(ii) So at this angle we have for red light $d \sin \theta = 2\lambda_R$
and for blue light $d \sin \theta = 3\lambda_B$

Consequently $2\lambda_R = 3\lambda_B$

Hence $\lambda_R = 675 \, \text{nm}$ *(1 mark)*

(iii) Using $d \sin \theta = 3\lambda_B$ we get

$\sin \theta = 3\lambda_B/d$ *(1 mark)*
$= 3 \times 450 \times 10^{-9} \times 3 \times 10^5$
$= 0.4050$

and the angle θ is $23.89°$ *(1 mark)*

(c) The condition for coincidence is $d \sin \theta = n\lambda_R = m\lambda_B$ where n and m are integers, but also where $\lambda_R = \frac{3}{2} \cdot \lambda_B$

Therefore for coincidence $\frac{3}{2} n = m$

i.e. $3n = 2m$

A further possibility satisfying this is $n = 4$ and $m = 6$ *(1 mark)*

Thus $d \sin \theta = 4\lambda_R$

giving $\sin \theta = \dfrac{4\lambda_R}{d} = 4 \times 675 \times 10^{-9} \times 3 \times 10^5$

$$= 0.81$$

Hence $\theta = 54°$

(*1 mark*)

Question 4

The initial p.d. across the capacitor is the maximum $= 12\,\text{V}$
Maximum charge $Q = CV = 470 \times 10^{-6} \times 12 = 5.64 \times 10^{-3}\,\text{C}$ (*1 mark*)

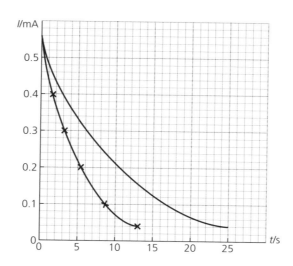

Initial current $= \dfrac{V}{R} = \dfrac{12}{22 \times 10^3} = 5.45 \times 10^{-4}\,\text{A}$, so large division on

y-axis $= 1 \times 10^{-4}\,\text{A} = 0.1\,\text{mA}$.

RC (time constant) is the time for the current to fall to

$\dfrac{5.45 \times 10^{-4}}{e} = 2.00 \times 10^{-4}\,\text{A}$ (2 large divisions on y-scale.)   (*2 marks*)

$RC = 470 \times 10^{-6} \times 22 \times 10^3 = 10.3\,\text{s}$. Hence 1 large division on x-axis $= 5\,\text{s}$.

(*2 marks*)

Adding a second $470\,\mu\text{F}$ capacitor in series make the total capacitance $235\,\mu\text{F}$ and hence the new charge stored $= 2.82 \times 10^{-3}\,\text{C}$.   (*1 mark*)

HINT

The initial current is the same, but the time taken to reach $2 \times 10^{-4}\,\text{A}$ has halved.

The second line on the graph shows how the current varies with time during discharge.   (*2 marks*)

The charge stored is equal to the *area* under the graph (half the original).

(*1 mark*)

Question 5

(a) (i) hf is the energy of a photon of the incident radiation.   (*1 mark*)

HINT

Compare the equation to $y = mx + c$

   (ii) The gradient $= h = 2 \times \dfrac{10^{-19}}{(6 - 3) \times 10^{14}} = 6.66 \times 10^{-34}\,\text{Js}$.   (*2 marks*)

(b) A photon with the minimum energy will release a photoelectron with
   energy $E_k = 0\,\text{J}$.

   From the graph, the frequency (threshold) of this photon $= 3.0 \times 10^{-14}\,\text{Hz}$

   Hence the energy $= hf = 6.66 \times 10^{-34} \times 3.0 \times 10^{-14} = 2.0 \times 10^{-19}\,\text{J}$

(*2 marks*)

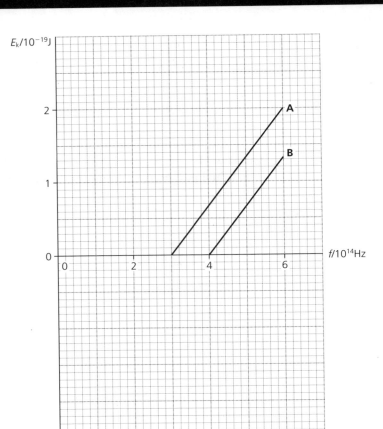

HINT

*The graph will have the same gradient h. A higher work function will mean the threshold frequency will need to be greater. Don't forget to label the line **B**.*

(c) $E_k/10^{-19}$ J

$f/10^{14}$ Hz

(2 marks)

Question 6

(a) Force on an ion $= Bqv$, where B is the field strength, q the charge on the ion and v is the speed of the ion. *(2 marks)*

(b) Electric field $= \dfrac{V}{d} = 600 \times \dfrac{10^{-6}}{1.4 \times 10^{-3}} = 0.42\,\text{NC}^{-1}$

Force $=$ field $\times$ charge $= 0.42 \times 1.6 \times 10^{-19} = 6.86 \times 10^{-20}\,\text{N}$

$= 6.9 \times 10^{-20}\,\text{N}$ *(2 marks)*

(c) The forces are equal so $Bqv = 6.86 \times 10^{20}$

(i) $v = \dfrac{6.86 \times 10^{-20}}{2.0 \times 1.6 \times 10^{-19}} = 0.21\,\text{m s}^{-1}$ *(2 marks)*

(ii) Volume per second $= v \times$ area $= 0.21 \times 1.5 \times 10^{-6} = 3.2 \times 10^{-7}\,\text{m}^3$ *(2 marks)*

LONGMAN EXAM PRACTICE KITS

REVISION PLANNER

Getting Started *Begin on week 12*

Use a calendar to put dates onto your planner and write in the dates of your exams. Fill in your targets for each day. Be realistic when setting the targets, and try your best to stick to them. If you miss a revision period, remember to re-schedule it for another time.

Get Familiar *Weeks 12 and 11*

Identify the topics on your syllabuses. Get to know the format of the papers – time, number of questions, types of questions. Start reading through your class notes, coursework, etc.

Get Serious *Week 10*

Complete reading through your notes – you should now have an overview of the whole syllabus. Choose 12 topics to study in greater depth for each subject. Allocate two topic areas for each subject for each of the next 6 weeks

No. of weeks before the exams	Date: Week commencing	MONDAY	TUESDAY
12			
11			
10			

WEDNESDAY	THURSDAY	FRIDAY	SATURDAY	SUNDAY

WEDNESDAY	THURSDAY	FRIDAY	SATURDAY	SUNDAY

No. of weeks before the exams	Date: Week commencing	MONDAY	TUESDAY
9			
8			
7			
6			
5			
4			
3			
2			
1			

Titles Available –

GCSE	A-LEVEL
Biology	Biology
Business Studies	British and European Modern History
Chemistry	Business Studies
English	Chemistry
French	Economics
Geography	French
German	Geography
Higher Maths	German
Information Systems	Mathematics
Mathematics	Physics
Physics	Psychology
Science	Sociology

There are lots of ways to revise. It is important to find what works best for you. Here are some suggestions:

- try testing with a friend: testing each other can be fun!
- label or highlight sections of text and make a checklist of these items.
- learn to write summaries – these will be useful for revision later.
- try reading out loud to yourself.
- don't overdo it – the most effective continuous revision session is probably between forty and sixty minutes long.
- practise answering past exam papers and test yourself using the same amount of time as you will have on the actual day – this will help to make the exam itself less daunting.
- pace yourself, taking it step by step.

WEDNESDAY	THURSDAY	FRIDAY	SATURDAY	SUNDAY

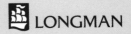